fundamentals
of
television

fundamentals
of
television

WALTER H. BUCHSBAUM

JOHN F. RIDER PUBLISHER, INC., NEW YORK
A division of Hayden Publishing Company, Inc.

PREFACE

The author of a technical work is not expected to provide more than the technical facts, but I hope that the readers of this book will gain an understanding of television as well as the ability to use it. My major aim in writing this book has been to stress the understanding of basic principles, because without this understanding a person cannot do a professional job.

A popular anecdote tells of an automobile mechanic who, after carefully listening to a coughing, sputtering engine, thought for a while, and then hit it once with his hammer. Instantly, the engine started running properly. When asked how he could charge ten dollars for such a simple repair, the mechanic broke down his charge as follows: one dollar for tapping the engine and nine dollars for knowing where. This story is an excellent illustration of the value of thinking out a servicing problem and the importance of understanding fundamentals *before* using the hammer. At a time when complaints about poor service of home appliances and stories of unreliable servicemen, unscrupulous operators, and excessive charges can be found almost daily in the newspapers, the service technician who "knows his stuff" will appear as a shining light in the community. The man who can handle all aspects of television servicing with professional competence cannot fail to do well, while the "amateur repairman" is bound to go under. Yet the main difference between them is nothing more than a thorough understanding of fundamentals.

Television sets are much too complex for the jack-of-all-trades, the handy fixer, or the screwdriver mechanic. While it is true that occasionally such a person is lucky enough to find a simple trouble, and that anyone can exchange tubes, it takes much more to install, align, and repair TV sets day after day. No one can expect to make a decent living from occasional lucky hits, but a thorough understanding of how television receivers work will usually guarantee good profits and a steady income.

v

Although this book contains alignment, installation, and trouble-shooting information, the main emphasis is on the fundamentals of television receivers. It is my hope that the reader will not skip over the theoretical part and will not be satisfied with a superficial grasp of the principles but will dig in until he understands clearly how the individual circuits really work. Once this effort is made, the rest of the study will become very easy. Once the fundamentals are understood, the troubleshooting and alignment techniques become self-evident and the student will find that he can locate most defects just from studying the circuit diagram. He will be able to "think out" a problem before having to dig into the chassis. When the student can think a problem through, when he bases his work on an understanding of television fundamentals, the major aim of this book has been achieved. He thinks before doing, and that is the mark of the professional. When servicing is based on knowledge and understanding, its success is assured. What is more, each problem solved contributes to future competence, because, only if we understand what we are testing or repairing, can we use this experience on similar problems later.

Here then is my personal advice to the reader, in brief. Try to understand the fundamentals. Use this understanding in solving a problem. Analyze a circuit first on paper and only then dig into the chassis.

No book of this type is possible without the assistance of the many manufacturers of TV receivers and components who make their technical data available to the author. I therefore want to thank all those manufacturers whose material appears here. I also want to thank the publishers who have offered constructive criticism and advice on many aspects of this text. The inspiration, forbearance, and encouragement of my wife was another essential ingredient which made this work possible. Lastly, I want to express my appreciation to Noreen Connor, who provided the efficient typing service which translated the draft into readable form.

New York
October, 1964   WALTER H. BUCHSBAUM

CONTENTS

vii

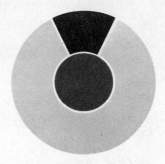

1   INTRODUCTION TO TELEVISION

Most of the readers of this book will barely remember the early days of television, let alone the years when radio broadcasting was the only wireless home entertainment. Before 1947, television was a rare thing used for occasional experimental transmissions, demonstrations, and, generally, as a laboratory curiosity. Not until early in 1947 did television sets begin to appear in the American home. Even then, home sets were a rarity, but their availability and popularity gained rapidly, so that today practically every home has at least one and frequently two receivers.

Television is now as much a part of our daily life as the automobile, the refrigerator, and other twentieth-century conveniences. A far cry from the early small screen, large cabinet, living-room monster, today's television sets are available in a host of screen and cabinet types and sizes, ranging from the transistor "pocket TV" set shown in Figure 1-1 to the color TV console of Figure 1-2. In between these two extremes of size and complexity is a wide range of models that fit into any kind of decorative scheme — models with clock timers and remote controls and models that combine with radio and audio equipment to form complete home entertainment centers.

Although the home entertainment aspect of television is the most conspicuous application of this technique of "seeing at a distance" (which is the meaning of the Greek *tele* and the Latin *vision*), television is used in many other capacities. Such unsung and routine jobs as monitoring steel rolling mills, iron ore chutes, and furnace operations are performed by television in all types of industrial installations. Color television is used to teach surgeons, to view X-ray photographs, to locate inaccessible obstructions in sewers, and to view atomic reactor operations too dangerous for

1

Fig. 1-1. A miniature transistorized TV set. (Sony Corp.)

humans to approach. Television cameras ride the weather satellites orbiting the earth and report on the cloud cover or warn us of storms. Television pictures have been sent back from the far side of the moon, which no human eye has ever seen without the assistance of TV. Television cameras travel on all types of manned spacecraft to show how the astronauts are getting along. There is hardly any activity involving the act of seeing where television is not used to assist the human operator.

All of these diverse television systems use the same fundamentals, whether the camera is on the ocean bottom or on the far side of the moon, or whether the picture shows a delicate heart operation in color or the flame of a rocket is monitored in the safety of the blockhouse. These fundamentals include not only the electronics necessary for transmitting television signals over a distance, but also the optical and mechanical principles utilized by the many different circuits, components, tubes, and other devices which comprise any television system. The means by which the television signal reaches the receiver do not matter. Whether it is just a short cable from the nuclear reactor to the control room or a telemetering link from a spacecraft, the fundamentals of television still apply.

Fig. 1-2. A color TV console. (RCA)

The television system is basically composed of two parts: the *transmitter,* which contains the camera, and the *receiver.* In every system there must be at least one transmitter, but there are usually several receivers. This book concentrates on the receiver, but explains the functions of the entire system to provide a proper understanding of all the signals and their functions. Since home television receivers form by far the largest field for servicing, the text is oriented to all types of home receivers. However, anyone who knows how to service home television sets will also be able to maintain and repair any other type of receiver.

Using This Text

Although television systems are extremely complex in comparison to ordinary house plumbing or various electrical appliances, an understanding of the fundamentals of television can be gained by any person of average intelligence with an aptitude for technical material. To grasp these fundamentals, it is not necessary to understand higher mathematics, nor is a college background essential. This text does assume that its reader understands the principles of electricity and magnetism, that he knows enough about radio to service receivers, and that he can use such simple test equipment as voltmeters, ohmmeters, etc. The ability to read circuit diagrams and understand simple waveform drawings and familiarity with resistance, capacitance, and inductance values are all taken for granted here. Anyone with some training or knowledge of electronics, whether audio, radio, communications (professional or amateur), industrial controls, and so on, will be able to learn the fundamentals of television.

With this background, the reader will have no difficulty following the text, which starts with an explanation of how television pictures are generated and then describes television picture tubes, which are the heart of the receiver. A review of transistors is followed by the principles of color television because color circuits and transistor circuits are treated along with the earlier black-and-white vacuum-tube circuits. After Chapter 5, each receiver function is treated in enough detail to provide a good understanding of its circuit fundamentals. With each receiver section are given basic alignment and troubleshooting procedures that are applicable to all types of sets. A special chapter (21) is devoted to installation problems and another chapter (22) covers the alignment steps to be performed in a typical color receiver. Because a color receiver contains all of the circuits required in a black-and-white receiver this last chapter provides a summary of all alignments necessary on television sets.

To learn most rapidly and most thoroughly, the reader should not skip through the book but should follow each chapter in sequence. He should never proceed to another portion or chapter until the preceding one has been understood. Once the reader has gone through the first few chapters, it will become obvious that all the material is arranged in such a manner as to build up technical knowledge gradually. Complex circuits always follow the simpler, more fundamental concepts. After the first five chapters, the reader will also notice that he can diagnose and repair more and more receiver defects as he progresses through the book. After the entire book has been studied, it will be worthwhile to keep it as a reference, especially since the end of each chapter contains a section on troubleshooting and alignment for the particular receiver section covered in that chapter.

PAINTING THE TELEVISION PICTURE

A picture, whether it is a painting or a photograph, contains many different components that must all be reproduced in a certain way to create a particular image in the observer's mind. As the majority of television receivers is still capable of showing only black and white pictures, a comparison of the TV picture with black and white moving pictures is in order.

When we watch movies we know that the scenes on the screen are produced by a sequence of separate, individual photographs that are flashed rapidly on the screen. In each successive picture all stationary objects are usually in exactly the same place, but moving objects are shown in progressively different positions. This sequence of still photographs is projected at a standard rate of 24 individual pictures or *frames* per second. Each frame is flashed on the screen, then a shutter blocks the projecting light while the film is moved to bring the next frame in front of the lens. This blocking action is necessary to prevent the motion of the film from being visible.

Television makes use of essentially the same technique. A complete TV picture appears on the screen 30 times a second. Between each picture there is an interval during which the screen is dark. In TV frames, also, stationary objects usually appear in the same place and moving objects appear to move because of slight changes in their position in subsequent frames. TV frames differ from movie frames, however, in that they are not projected as a complete picture. With the transparent movie film, the picture elements block the projection light enough to produce the different shades of gray that make up a complete black and white picture. In television, the picture is created in sections by varying the brightness of a moving spot of light.

SCANNING

To understand how a picture is produced by a moving spot of light, consider the effect produced by the light beam of a sharply-focused flashlight when it is moved over a flat surface. When the flashlight is slowly moved from side to side, the spot of its beam on a screen moves sideways. When the flashlight is moved rapidly from side to side, however, the entire path of the spot appears to be illuminated and the light beam produces a horizontal line instead of a spot (Figure 2-1B). This effect, like the sequential frame projection used in movies, is created by what we call *persistence of vision*. The human eye retains an impression for many hundredths of a second and cannot distinguish fast changes. Events

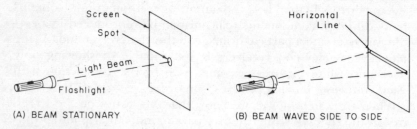

Fig. 2-1. The principle of scanning can be illustrated with a moving flashlight beam.

that occur faster than this retention period are either unnoticed or, if they are repetitive, appear to be continuous to the human observer. A complete picture or frame is produced in this fashion in television. Inside the picture tube, an electron gun generates an electron beam that acts somewhat like the flashlight beam. This beam moves very rapidly across a phosphor-coated screen and, by changing its strength, produces different amounts of light in different places. To be precise, the electron beam is focused into a fine point that moves from the upper left-hand corner in a straight horizontal line to the right side of the screen.

Figure 2-2 shows how the picture tube screen is scanned to "paint" the TV picture. During each motion from left to right, the electron beam is varied in intensity and thus paints a line of the picture. During the return motion from right to left, the beam intensity is reduced so that no light is produced and the beam is moved down a little on the tube face.

The speed of the beam's motion from left to right and back again is so great that it covers the entire tube face and "paints" a

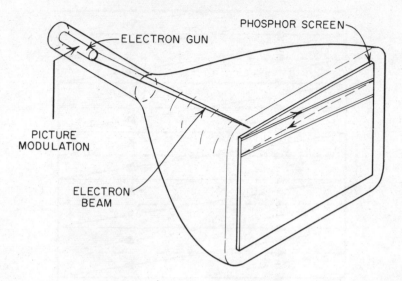

Fig. 2-2. "Painting" the TV picture.

complete picture thirty times a second. This great speed is possible because an electron beam in a vacuum has no appreciable inertia and no friction is involved. The motion of the electron beam is called *scanning,* but the electronic actions involved are generally referred to as *sweeping* and we speak of a *horizontal sweep frequency* of 15,750 cycles per second.

Interlaced Scanning. In actual television practice, the horizontal scanning process does not use the simple pattern of going from the first line to the second and then to the third. Instead, all odd-numbered lines are scanned first and then all even-numbered lines are scanned. Figure 2-3 shows how the electron beam scans the screen. Since the entire frame is painted in 1/30 of a second, a complete set of odd or even lines, called a *field,* must be painted in 1/60 of a second. By making the field rate 60 cycles per second, the susceptibility of the picture to apparent flicker is greatly reduced because changes at that high rate are completely invisible to the human eye. This scanning pattern is called *interlaced scanning* and is similar to the double shutter technique used in movies. (Although the movie frames change at the 24 per second rate, the shutter is closed twice during each frame to obtain a flicker rate —48 per second—that is much faster than the human eye can follow.) The illuminated area produced by the scanning lines on the picture tube face is called a *raster.*

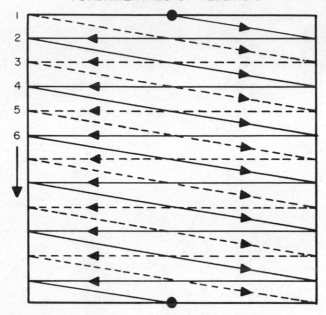

Fig. 2-3. An interlaced scanning pattern.

PICTURE SYNCHRONIZATION

In the movies, the picture information is completely contained in the film, but in television, the picture information is obtained from a transmitter that may be many miles away. Neglecting for the time being the transmission path and its problems, it is fairly obvious that there must be some connection between the picture seen by the television camera and that shown on the screen. Using movie film again for an analogy, we know what happens if the film speed in the theater is different from the speed at which the movie was made. People either seem to move very fast or else very slow. The speed of the movie projector must be the same as that of the camera used to make the movie.

In television, the problem of speed synchronization is much more severe. If the receiver scans a picture in more or less than 1/30 of a second, there will be room at the bottom of the screen; the picture will appear to roll vertically, either from top to bottom or bottom to top. If the frame rate at the receiver is 15 cps, then two complete pictures will appear, one above the other. If the line scanning is not exactly the same at the receiver and transmitter, the picture will appear torn into strips or sliced into diagonal slices. For these reasons, great care is taken to synchronize accurately the scanning of each line and frame. The transmitting station provides synchronizing signals to the camera and the same synchronizing signals are sent out together with the sound and picture information.

Figure 2-4 shows the basic elements of a complete television transmitter and receiver system. To reproduce the picture it is necessary to transmit horizontal and vertical synchronizing signals,

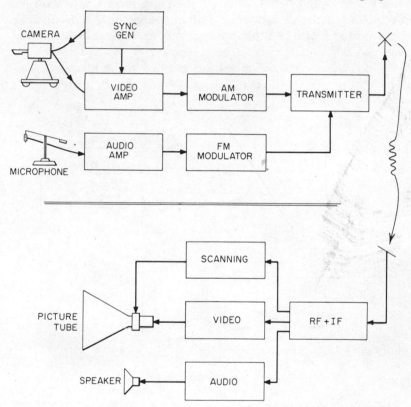

Fig. 2-4. The basic elements of the television transmitter and receiver system.

as well as brightness information. The synchronizing signals are in the form of pulses which occur at the beginning of each horizontal line and at the start of each vertical field. Picture or video information is only available during the time when the electron beam moves from left to right, so it can only start after the horizontal sync pulse has occurred.

The TV Camera

The television camera has an optical system similar to that of a movie camera, but a light-sensitive plate inside a vacuum tube is used instead of film. As illustrated in Figure 2-5, this plate is scanned by an electron beam that changes in current intensity according to the light pattern on the plate. The actual picture information is contained in this varying beam current, which is amplified. This video signal, when applied to a picture tube, will reproduce what the camera sees. Camera tubes have become very sophisticated and a host of different models are available, selling under such names as Vidicon, Image Orthicon, etc. Note, in Figure 2-5, that the same sync pulses are applied to both camera and picture tube to keep the two electron beams exactly in step.

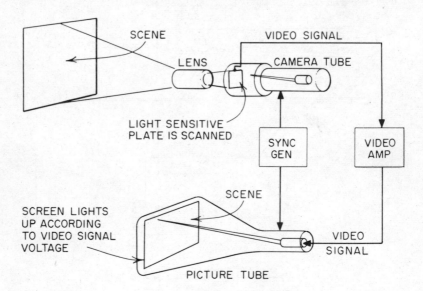

Fig. 2-5. The basic elements of the television camera and picture tube.

BLACK, GREY, AND WHITE

Video Signals. Actual television signals are a little more complex than we have indicated because, in addition to starting each line, the edges of the picture must be blanked out to avoid any appearance of slightly ragged edges and the electron beam must be turned off during the time in which it returns to the starting place. This return time is called the *retrace* or *flyback period* and is approximately 9 microseconds long for each line, but considerably longer for the period when the beam returns from the bottom to the top of the screen.

A typical signal for one line of picture is shown in Figure 2-6; the dotted line indicates the so-called *black level* at which the picture tube is blanked out. Note that at the beginning of each line the sync pulse is well in the black region and that during the entire retrace period the signal is black. The sync pulse is shorter than the retrace interval to allow the receiver circuitry a short period in which the actual synchronizing can take place. In the chapter on synchronization, the need for this will become clearer.

To get an idea of the way the video signal paints the picture, consider the line near the top of the picture in Figure 2-7 and the corresponding video signal shown above it. Note how the various shades of lighter and darker picture portions correspond to higher and lower voltage levels. The edges of the picture are completely black because the blanking pulse is high enough to extend into the black region.

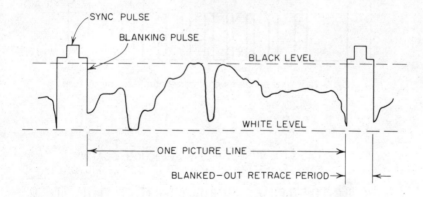

Fig. 2-6. The video signal for one TV picture line.

Signal Standards

The start of each field or vertical scanning is also indicated by a sync pulse. The vertical pulse period lasts much longer than the horizontal sync pulses. It is approximately 22 times as long as the

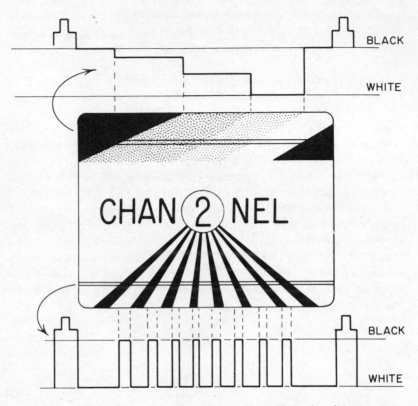

Fig. 2-7. How the video signal corresponds to the picture.

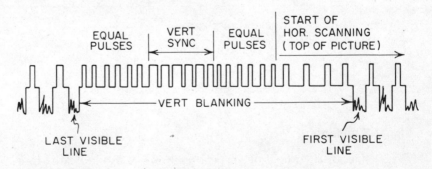

Fig. 2-8. The vertical sync pulse.

horizontal sweep period. To avoid losing the horizontal sync during the vertical retrace period, the horizontal sync pulses are superimposed on the vertical blanking pulse, as shown in Figure 2-8. The first six horizontal pulses are very narrow and are called *equalizing pulses.* After the equalizing pulses come six wide pulses which are the actual vertical sync pulse, serrated at the horizontal sync period. This is followed by another six equalizing pulses and then four regular horizontal pulses that start the top of the picture. Note that the blanking period extends throughout this time and darkens the screen while the beam moves from bottom to top and covers the first four lines. Actually, every alternate vertical sync period contains only three blanked top lines because alternate fields start at line 1 or line 2, respectively, to provide the interlaced scanning described earlier.

The television signal, as we have seen, is quite different from the audio signal heard through the radio. It contains two sync signals in addition to the video signal that reproduces the picture. While the human ear can detect sound frequencies between 20 cycles and about 15,000 cycles, the eye is much more sensitive. With normal vision, we distinguish a great amount of fine detail, such as this printing or the checkerboard pattern of the bottom of the picture of Figure 2-7. To reproduce this fine detail, the video signal, as shown in the single line at the bottom of Figure 2-7, must change rapidly from black to white. This means that the video signal must contain high frequencies. Television standards in the United States provide for a video signal ranging from 30 cps to about 4 mc, which gives sufficient picture resolution to see a dot that is as wide as a scanning line is high. The actual size of a horizontal line depends on the focus, the screen size, and the adjustment of the set, but there are always 525 lines in a full frame, or 262.5 in each 60 cps field in American TV sets.

TV Audio Signal. So far we have only considered the picture portion of the television system. The sound picked up over the microphone must also be transmitted to produce the proper sound and picture at the receiver. At the studio, the sound is amplified in the same manner as in broadcast systems and is frequency modulated at the transmitter. The frequency modulation standards are slightly different than those used for FM broadcast stations, but the principles are the same. A detailed discussion of frequency modulation will be found in Chapter 18, which covers the audio section.

TABLE 2-1

Chan. No.	Frequency Band (MC)	Video Carrier	Audio Carrier	Chan. No.	Frequency Band (MC)	Video Carrier	Audio Carrier
2	54-60	55.25	59.75	43	644-650	645.25	649.75
3	60-66	61.25	65.75	44	650-656	651.25	655.75
4	66-72	67.25	71.75	45	656-662	657.25	661.75
5	76-82	77.25	81.75	46	662-668	663.25	667.75
6	82-88	83.25	87.75	47	668-674	669.25	673.75
7	174-180	175.25	179.75	48	674-680	675.25	679.75
8	180-186	181.25	185.75	49	680-686	681.25	685.75
9	186-192	187.25	191.75	50	686-692	687.25	691.75
10	192-198	193.25	197.75	51	692-698	693.25	697.75
11	198-204	199.25	203.75	52	698-704	699.25	703.75
12	204-210	205.25	209.75	53	704-710	705.25	709.75
13	210-216	211.25	215.75	54	710-716	711.25	715.75
14	470-476	471.25	475.75	55	716-722	717.25	721.75
15	476-482	477.25	481.75	56	722-728	723.25	727.75
16	482-488	483.25	487.75	57	728-734	729.25	733.75
17	488-494	489.25	493.75	58	734-740	735.25	739.75
18	494-500	495.25	499.75	59	740-746	741.25	745.75
19	500-506	501.25	505.75	60	746-752	747.25	751.75
20	506-512	507.25	511.75	61	752-758	753.25	757.75
21	512-518	513.25	517.75	62	758-764	759.25	763.75
22	518-524	519.25	523.75	63	764-770	765.25	769.75
23	524-530	525.25	529.75	64	770-776	771.25	775.75
24	530-536	531.25	535.75	65	776-782	777.25	781.75
25	536-542	537.25	541.75	66	782-788	783.25	787.75
26	542-548	543.25	547.75	67	788-794	789.25	793.75
27	548-554	549.25	553.75	68	794-800	795.25	799.75
28	554-560	555.25	559.75	69	800-806	801.25	805.75
29	560-566	561.25	565.75	70	806-812	807.25	811.75
30	566-572	567.25	571.75	71	812-818	813.25	817.75
31	572-578	573.25	577.75	72	818-824	819.25	823.75
32	578-584	579.25	583.75	73	824-830	825.25	829.75
33	584-590	585.25	589.75	74	830-836	831.25	835.75
34	590-596	591.25	595.75	75	836-842	837.25	841.75
35	596-602	597.25	601.75	76	842-848	843.25	847.75
36	602-608	603.25	607.75	77	848-854	849.25	853.75
37	608-614	609.25	613.75	78	854-860	855.25	859.75
38	614-620	615.25	619.75	79	860-866	861.25	865.75
39	620-626	621.25	625.75	80	866-872	867.25	871.75
40	626-632	627.25	631.75	81	872-878	873.25	877.75
41	632-638	633.25	637.75	82	878-884	879.25	883.75
42	638-644	639.25	643.75	83	884-890	885.25	889.75

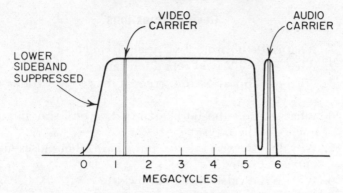

Fig. 2-9. The TV channel spectrum.

TV CHANNELS

The picture and sound information is transmitted in the same channel, but actually uses different carriers. As shown in Figure 2-9, the sound carrier is located 4.5-mc higher in frequency than the picture carrier and, while the sound carrier is frequency modulated by the audio signal, the picture carrier is amplitude modulated in an unusual fashion. If a 4-mc wide signal modulates an r-f carrier, it will produce a lower and upper sideband, each up to 4 mc from the center carrier frequency. This would mean that a band at least 8-mc wide would be required for the picture transmission alone. Since only one of these sidebands will be used after detection, one of them can be omitted. (This principle is used in single sideband communications systems.) In television, the total channel width is 6 mc, which is possible because most of the lower sideband is suppressed at the transmitter.

Channel Frequencies. Figure 2-9 shows the spectrum distribution of a TV channel according to the U.S. transmission standards. Table 2-1 shows the actual frequency allotment for each of the 82 television channels authorized in the United States. Channel numbers start at 2 and are commonly divided into the low vhf band, channels 2–6, the high vhf band, channels 7–13, and the uhf band, which includes channels 14 through 83. Outside the U.S., only Canada has the same standards. In Europe most television stations operate at 625 lines, except for France where up to 800 lines are used. Instead of 60-cps field rates, 50 cps is common abroad because those are the power-line frequencies.

Review Questions

1. What is the horizontal scanning frequency?
2. What is the TV field repetition rate?
3. What will appear on the screen if the receiver frame rate is 15 cps?
4. What controls the horizontal and vertical scanning frequency at the receiver?
5. Why does the vertical sync pulse have other pulses superimposed on it?
6. What is the video signal bandwidth?
7. What is the relation of sound to video r-f carrier?
8. Are both sidebands transmitted in TV?
9. What channels fall into the high vhf band?
10. What channels fall into the uhf band?

THE PICTURE TUBE

The heart of the television set is undoubtedly the picture tube. Except for the audio portion, all the electronic circuits in the set work for the picture tube because it converts the electrical signals into something the human can appreciate—the picture. At the studio the camera converts the scene into a series of electrical signals; at the receiver the picture tube reverses the process. We have seen in Chapter 2 how the screen is scanned to "paint" the picture in the form of individual lines and frames. The detailed process by which the picture is actually reproduced on the screen of the picture tube will be covered in this chapter.

All picture tubes are really large glass bottles, sometimes with metal sides, that contain a fairly good vacuum. The end of this glass bottle that is relatively flat is where the screen material is deposited. Picture tubes are available in different screen sizes, most of which are rectangular. The screen size, measured in inches diagonally across the screen, is indicated in the first two numbers of the picture tube type number. The 27AP4 of Figure 3-1 indicates that the tube has a 27-inch diagonal screen; P4 stands for the type of phosphor used. (For monochrome television, all tubes use P4 because it has the specified color and other characteristics for black-and-white TV displays.) The letters between the screen size and the phosphor type indicate the particular tube type and are issued to manufacturers by the Electronic Industries Association (EIA) as new tube types become available. Almost all of the picture tubes found in sets since 1955 will have a rectangular screen. Some consist entirely of glass. while a portion of the cone of others is made of metal. Metal tubes are lighter and have some other advantages, but they also have some disadvantages as we shall see

17

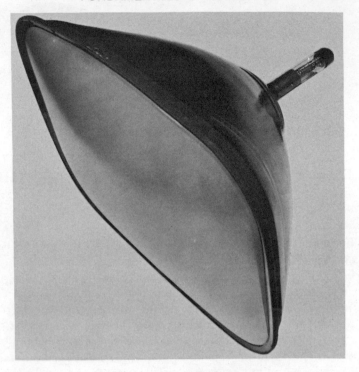

Fig. 3-1. A typical picture tube, type 27AP4. (Rauland Corp.)

in the following discussion. Picture tubes have an *aspect ratio* of 4:3, meaning that the ratio of width to height is always in that proportion. A picture 20 inches wide will be 15 inches high. This ratio is one at which figures on the screen are most life-like. At other ratios, people and things appear to be too thin or too wide.

BASIC PICTURE TUBE FUNCTIONS

We already know that the picture tube uses an electron beam to "paint" a picture on the screen. This means that it must contain some elements to generate such an electron beam, some means to control the beam's motion, and, finally, a screen. In most respects, the television picture tube is similar to the cathode-ray tubes used in oscilloscopes. The name *cathode-ray tube* (CRT) originated many years ago when experiments with vacuum tubes indicated that phosphor would glow when located near a cathode. Actually, the tuning eye tube found in FM tuners uses the same principle. Electrons are emitted from the heated cathode and attracted towards the anode, which is at a positive potential. As they move from the cathode to the anode, they strike a layer of phosphor material that will glow in proportion to the energy and quantity of the electrons hitting it. In the picture tube, the electrons emitted from the cathode are focused into a stream that hits the phosphor at one tiny spot. When the stream is moved back and forth, the tiny spot describes a line.

Picture Tube Elements. Figure 3-2 illustrates the basic parts found in the picture tube. The *electron gun* contains an arrangement of elements that generates the *electron beam* and also controls its intensity. A *focusing element* in front of the electron gun focuses the beam into a spot. (As will be shown later, focusing can be done either electrostatically or magnetically; either method achieves the same result — the beam converges as a very small, round spot on

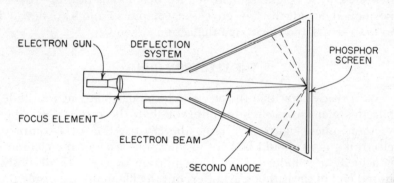

Fig. 3-2. The basic picture tube elements.

the screen.) The *screen* is a slightly curved surface coated with a phosphor mixture that lights up when struck by a strong concentration of electrons. To attract the electrons and give them the required speed, a conducting coating deposited inside the tube in a ring around the screen forms the *anode.* Electrons bouncing off the screen are attracted to the anode coating and returned into the circuit. Picture tubes with a metal envelope use that envelope as the second anode, which means that, for safety's sake, the metal envelope must be covered by a plastic, high-voltage insulation jacket. Connection to the metal envelope is made through a spring action contact inside the plastic jacket that goes to a snap button on the outside. The high voltage connector then goes to that snap button. In all-glass tubes the second anode is a graphite coating on the inside of the glass envelope. A recessed metal well is the high voltage contact into which the high voltage connector fits. A good glass tube performs just as well as a good metal envelope type, but manufacturing procedures at different plants make one type or the other more economical for a particular manufacturer.

The remaining element in the picture tube is the *deflection system*. This must perform two functions at the same time. It must sweep the electron beam from left to right and back at the horizontal sweep rate of 15,750 cps, and it must also move the beam down and up again at the 60 cps vertical sweep rate. For this reason the deflection system consists of two parts: the *horizontal sweep* and the *vertical sweep*. Although a few earlier television sets used deflection plates inside the picture tube, like the small screen CRT's used in oscilloscopes, practically all modern sets now use electromagnetic deflection. This means that the electron beam is deflected by a magnetic field set up by current flowing in coils positioned outside the tube envelope. Chapters 7 and 8 are devoted to the vertical and horizontal deflection systems.

THE ELECTRON GUN

We already know that the electron beam originates at a cathode, but this element is slightly different than the cathode in other vacuum tubes. Figure 3-3 shows the cross-section of a complete electron gun (it should be kept in mind that each of the elements is actually a cylinder). The active portion of the cathode is the closed end of the cathode cylinder, but the filaments are inside the entire cylinder. Unlike the control grid in vacuum tubes, the grid element here is another cylinder, surrounding the cathode with a small opening opposite the active cathode portion. As in other vacuum tubes, the potential between the control grid and the cathode determines the number of electrons emitted from the cathode. If the grid element is at the same potential as the cathode, or slightly more positive, the maximum beam current will be produced. As the grid becomes progressively more negative with respect to the cathode, fewer electrons pass through the grid hole and the electron current diminishes. Most picture tubes have a grid cut-off voltage of about −50 to −65 volts, which means that when the grid is that much negative with respect to the cathode, so little beam current will flow that the screen is completely dark.

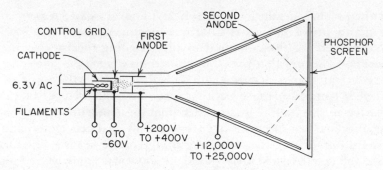

Fig. 3-3. The cross-sectional view of a complete electron gun.

Following the control grid is another cylindrical element called the *screen grid, first anode,* or *accelerator.* Its function is the same as that of the screen grid in a tetrode vacuum tube; it accelerates electrons passing it and attracts those few electrons that have bounced off the second anode. As shown in Figure 3-3, different voltages are applied to different elements in the electron gun, ranging from the relatively small voltage of the control grid to the very high, second anode voltage. It is this high voltage, generally at least 12,000 volts, that gives the electron beam its high speed. When the electron beam strikes the phosphor screen, individual electrons excite individual phosphor atoms and free electrons bounce off and drift toward the second anode. The high positive potential will attract any free electrons.

Along with the basic electron gun elements indicated in Figure 3-3, two additional elements are required for proper operation. These are discussed in the following paragraphs.

ION TRAPS

No matter how good the vacuum, there will always be a small amount of gas inside the picture-tube envelope. When electrons in the beam strike these gas atoms, they will either free or add an electron to the atomic structure, producing either a positive or negative charge. Such atoms are called *ions.* The negatively-charged ions will eventually be attracted to the second anode and cause no further trouble.

Ion Spot Elimination. Ions are much heavier than electrons and therefore are not deflected or focused into the electron beam. Instead, they bombard the screen·somewhere around the center and eventually burn it, causing a brown spot known as an *ion spot*. To avoid this problem, picture-tube manufacturers use one of two possible methods. One method involves coating the back of the phosphor screen with a very thin aluminum coat so that ions cannot penetrate it, but electrons can. This also increases the apparent screen brightness because light radiated into the picture tube is reflected to the front. The second system for eliminating ion spots uses the fact that electrons are deflected by magnetic force and ions are not. Within the electron gun, the entire beam is tilted to strike the positively-charged anode, as shown in Figure 3-4. This

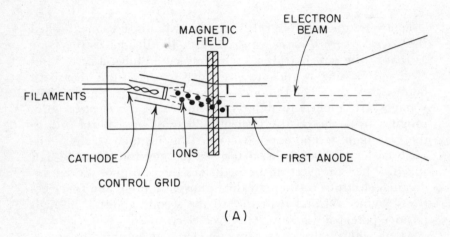

(A)

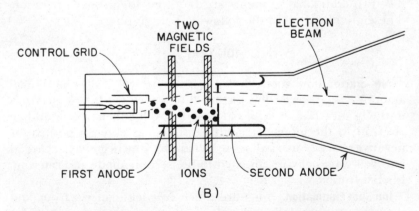

(B)

Fig. 3-4. Ion trap types: (A) the bent-gun ion trap; (B) the double magnet ion trap.

traps the ions by sending them directly to the anode but it also cuts off the electron beam from the phosphor screen. This is remedied by introducing a magnetic field, external to the electron gun, that bends the electron beam away from the anode so that it does strike the screen. This external magnet arrangement is called a *beam bender* or *ion trap* and must be carefully adjusted on the neck of the picture tube to produce a raster on the screen. If the magnet is misadjusted so that corners on the screen are cut off this means that at that point the electron beam is hitting the anode instead of the screen.

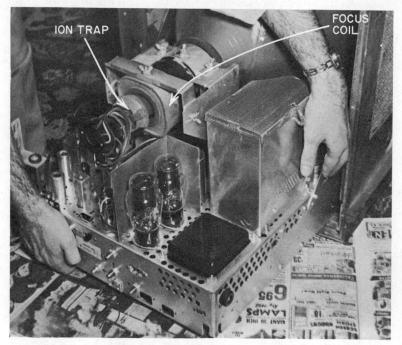

Fig. 3-5. A typical ion trap assembly.

Figure 3-5 shows a typical ion trap magnet assembly located on the neck of the picture tube. Ordinarily, this part is adjusted when it is placed on the neck of the tube and need only be readjusted when the picture tube is replaced or when one of the other components on the picture tube has been removed. There are two types of traps on the market, depending on the type of electron gun used. The majority of sets have an ion trap that consists of two rings of magnetic material, as shown in Figure 3-6. These types should always be mounted so that the thinner magnetic ring faces toward the screen. A single magnetic bar clamped to two steel pole pieces, as shown in Figure 3-7, is the second type of trap. Here, the polarity depends on the right-left orientation of the pole pieces. Before removing such a beam bender it is wise to mark the pole piece and the corresponding spot on the tube neck with a grease pencil, so that it will be easy to replace it. In either type, the trap adjustment is started by placing it close to the picture tube socket and rotating it slowly while moving it gradually towards the screen. During the adjustment, the picture tube screen should be observed, if necessary through a mirror, with the brightness control turned up to maximum. By careful adjustment it must be possible to fill the entire screen and get even brightness in the center as well as at each of the corners. Occasionally, the focus coil must also be adjusted to get rid of shadows in the corners (this will be discussed in the next section).

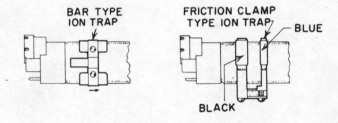

Fig. 3-6. Double magnet ion traps.

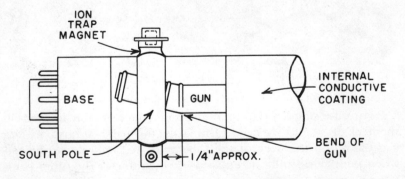

Fig. 3-7. A single magnet ion trap.

FOCUS

To get a sharp round spot on the screen the electron beam is focused like a light beam. This is accomplished in two different ways, depending on the type of picture tube used. The electron beam can either be focused electrostatically or magnetically.

Electrostatic Focus. To get electrostatic focus action, the second anode, or accelerator, must be divided into two portions and an electrostatic field set up. Figure 3-8 shows a typical arrangement used in almost all recent picture tubes. When the high voltage field of the second anode is interrupted by a field of much lower voltage, electrostatic lines of force are formed that bend the electron stream as illustrated. We speak of an electrostatic lens action because the action of the focusing element here is the same as that of the two curved surfaces of a regular double optical lens.

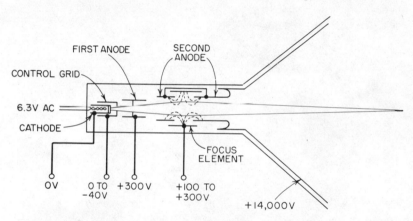

Fig. 3-8. A typical arrangement of elements for low-voltage electrostatic focus.

In general, the focusing potential is not too critical in this type of picture tube and in some sets the focus element is connected to a point on a bleeder resistor instead of a potentiometer. When the picture tube is replaced it may be necessary to connect the focus element to another point on the bleeder, but good focus is ordinarily obtained without much adjustment. The location of the beam bender on such picture tubes is not affected by the focusing since the electron beam is focused further on in the electron gun and there is no magnetic interaction.

Magnetic Focus. Magnetic focusing, generally found on older TV sets, uses an external device. This can be either a focus coil or a permanent magnet (PM) focus assembly, as shown in Figure 3-9. Focus coils use the B+ current to generate a magnetic field and act as bleeders and filters as part of the power supply. Whether a coil or a PM assembly is used, the principle of operation is the same. As shown in Figure 3-10, a circular magnetic field surrounds the electron beam and generates magnetic lines or force through which the electrons must pass. Those electrons traveling in the center of the beam are not affected since the magnetic field is zero at the center. Those electrons whose paths point outward from the beam cross the magnetic lines of force at such an angle that they are bent back towards the center.

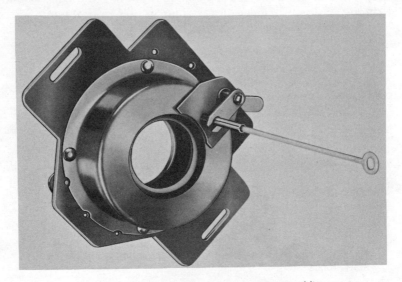

Fig. 3-9. A permanent magnet focus assembly.

Either type of magnetic focusing device (coil or PM) must be located at just the right spot on the neck of the picture tube or else it will be impossible to get uniform focus across the entire screen. The ring magnetic field must also be centered around the beam. Moving the focus device up or down will move the electron beam right or left. Moving it right or left will move the beam up or down.

Focus coils or PM units are mounted on special brackets with adjustment screws to permit some amount of centering and tilting

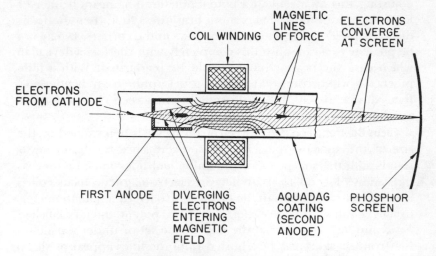

Fig. 3-10. How the magnetic focus operates.

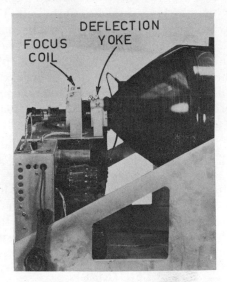

Fig. 3-11. The focus coil mounting.

of the focus device, as shown in Figure 3-11. In adjusting the focus
device, the first step is to center it so that the raster is centered
on the screen. In some TV sets a separate centering magnet is
employed for this and some very old sets control the centering
by passing a small amount of dc through the deflection coils and

adjusting this by means of a potentiometer. The beam bender or ion trap is adjusted for maximum brightness first, then the focus device is tilted to eliminate any shadows in the corners. It may not be possible to accomplish this completely with the focus device, in which case the beam bender should be readjusted. With a little practice it will become quite simple to set up the beam bender and focus device to get a full, uniformly bright screen. To get focus is another matter.

Focus Control. Focus of the electron beam is determined by the size of the spot on the screen. However, since the beam never stands still, the sharpness of the individual lines must be used as indication of good focus. When an electromagnetic focus coil is used, the current through the coil is controlled by a potentiometer, usually connected across the coil. This potentiometer, labelled *Focus* and located either at the rear of the set or under a panel in the front or side, may be adjusted until the lines appear as sharp as possible across the entire screen. In some sets, perfect focus may not be possible over the entire screen and a compromise must be reached between the blur of the line at the center or at the edge.

PM focus devices control the strength of the magnetic field by the size of the air gap between the front and back pole pieces. Usually, a lead screw is turned to move the pole pieces closer together or further apart. In some sets this screw is reached through an opening in the rear cover and should be adjusted with a non-magnetic screwdriver that does not distort the magnetic field so that repeated touch-up adjustments are required. Many sets include a flexible shaft arrangement which ends in a knurled knob that permits the lead screw to be turned directly by hand from the back of the set.

A general rule that applies to all magnetically focused picture tubes and which also holds true for beam benders is that any of these control devices should be located as close to the picture tube socket as possible while still getting the desired results.

CENTERING

As indicated previously, magnetically focused picture tubes require careful setting of the focus device to center the raster on the picture tube screen. In most such sets, the only centering adjustment provided is the mechanical mounting of the focusing device. Receivers that employ electrostatic focus, however, usually require a separate centering magnet. This looks very similar to the ion trap shown in Figure 3-6 and is located approximately where the focus device lies in magnetically focused sets. The centering assembly is merely a set of two ring magnets, each of which has an air gap. The picture is centered by rotating the rings. It is possible, by moving one ring's air gap from two to four o'clock, to move the raster up or down. The second ring's air gap can be set to twelve o'clock to move the raster left or right. Each of the rings has a tab attached that is manipulated to achieve any desired centering. A little actual experimentation will quickly indicate which way the tabs should be rotated to center the raster.

DEFLECTION

The interaction between magnetic lines of force and the electron beam makes possible the elimination of ion spots and is also used to focus the electron beam on the screen. Important as these functions are, all of them can also be performed by electrostatic lines of force that are generated right inside the picture tube envelope. It is also possible to deflect the electron beam to paint the picture by electrostatic means. The cathode-ray tubes used in oscilloscopes and in many radar displays use electrostatic deflection. Early, small-screen television sets employed electrostatically-deflected picture tubes, but for the modern, large-screen receivers magnetic deflection has become the standard method.

Electrostatic Deflection. In the electrostatic system a set of plates attracts and repels the electrons in the beam, as positive and negative voltage is applied to opposite plates. Using one set of opposing plates for horizontal deflection and another for vertical sweeping, the entire raster is created. To move the electron beam from left to right, the voltage on the horizontal deflection plates must be varied gradually and when the beam is returned to the left, the voltage must change in the opposite direction, but much faster. The resulting waveform is that of a sawtooth, with the more gradual slope corresponding to the picture portion and the steep, narrow portion providing the much faster return trace.

Magnetic Deflection. In modern television receivers the electron beam is deflected by a magnetic field passing through the glass neck of the picture tube. Two such fields are required separately, one for the vertical sweep and one for the horizontal sweep. These magnetic fields are generated by current passing through a set of coils located in a special assembly around the neck of the tube. Since the magnetic field depends entirely on the current through the coils, this current must have a sawtooth waveform, just like the sawtooth voltage waveform used in electrostatic deflection.

Magnetic deflection is presented in more detail in Chapters 7 and 8. At this point, however, a description of the mechanical arrangement of components on the picture tube would be incomplete without showing the deflection yoke. Figures 3-5 and 3-11 show the location of the deflection yoke on the neck of the picture tube. It is invariably as close to the screen as possible and the only adjustment it needs is a limited amount of rotation about the tube neck to level the edge of the raster with the edge of the screen. This adjustment only requires loosening a thumbscrew, rotating the deflection yoke until the raster is level, and then tightening the screw again.

Review Questions

1. How can we know the screen size from the type number?
2. Name three elements of the picture tube.
3. Name the four parts of the electron gun.
4. What controls the number of electrons in the beam?
5. What determines the speed of the electrons in the beam?
6. Name two methods for avoiding ion spots.
7. Which of the two parts of a double magnet beam bender goes towards the screen?
8. What forms the "electrostatic lens" force?
9. For magnetic focusing is the field longitudinal, transverse, or circular?
10. Name two methods of centering the picture.

TRANSISTOR FUNDAMENTALS

Transistors are but one product of the *semiconductor field,* which gets it name from the special materials whose electrical characteristics fall between the conductors and the insulators. Most materials either conduct electricity, which means they contain a surplus of free electrons, or else they are insulators, which means they have no free electrons at all. A few materials, such as silicon and germanium, form a special crystalline structure which, although essentially an insulator, can be made to conduct if small impurities are introduced. Depending on the type of impurity, the base metal contains either a surplus or a shortage of electrons. When a surplus of electrons exists, that type of semiconductor is called *n-type;* a semiconductor with a shortage of electrons is called *p-type.* By themselves, p- and n-type materials have no practical use, but when they are joined together they perform a vital electronic function.

SEMICONDUCTOR DIODES

Figure 4-1 shows the junction of a piece of p-type and a piece of n-type semiconductor material. Depending on the polarity of the voltage applied to the junction, current can either flow or not flow. If a voltage is such as to force the free electrons in the n-type and the "holes," or electron-deficient atoms, in the p-type material away from the junction, electrons cannot cross the junction and no current flows. If the voltage is reversed, current flows readily.

31

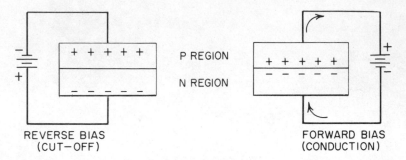

REVERSE BIAS   FORWARD BIAS
(CUT—OFF)   (CONDUCTION)

Fig. 4-1. Semiconductor diodes.

Electrons can only move from the surplus to the shortage area because of the p and n properties of the material. This unidirectional electron current flow is the cause of the diode or rectification function of the transistors.

Transistors consist of two such p-n diodes, joined as illustrated in Figure 4-2. In this example, the center section is made of n-type material and the two outer portions are p-type. This is called a *p-n-p transistor*. (Its opposite arrangement, an n-p-n transistor requires the exact opposite battery polarities.) The right element, receiving the negative battery voltage, is usually called the *collector* and the left element is called the *emitter*. If we try to find vacuum-tube analogs, we would compare the collector to the plate, the emitter to the cathode, and the center, called the *base,* to the control grid. This is an apt comparison because relatively small changes on the base have a larger effect on the total current.

TRANSISTORS AND VACUUM TUBES

Transistors are fundamentally different from tubes not only because they need no filament heater, but also because they are current devices, whereas tubes are basically voltage devices. Of course, voltage and current in a circuit are always related, but in transistors it is primarily the amount of base current that controls the collector current and transistor data are given in terms of these currents; tube data are given in terms of control voltages. Another great difference between tubes and transistors is the arrangement of impedances. In vacuum tubes the grid is a high impedance circuit while the plate has a much lower internal impedance. Transistor base impedance is usually very low and the collector or output impedance is much higher. In many transistor amplifiers, the in-

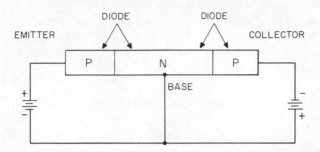

Fig. 4-2. The transistor consists of two diodes.

put and output voltages are almost the same and we only realize the gain of the amplifier by measuring the output current. Impedance matching is of prime consideration in transistor circuits and actual impedances are more critical than they are in vacuum-tube equipments.

Transistors and Temperature. Just as in the case of tubes, transistors are available for different power levels. Since the transistor is a relatively efficient device, it can be made quite small, but when power must be dissipated, the transistor size must be increased to provide sufficient surface to carry the heat away. Most power transistors that handle more than about half a watt will be mounted on a special heat sink that helps to dissipate the heat generated. These transistors should never be operated without this heat sink because, unlike vacuum tubes, all semiconductor devices are highly temperature-sensitive. Transistor data are always specified at a definite temperature because transistor operating characteristics change considerably with temperature.

Two transistor parameters in particular vary greatly with temperature: the collector leakage current and the base-to-emitter voltage drop. The collector leakage current is the current drawn with the transistor at cut-off and varies approximately 6% to 8% per degree centigrade. As temperature increases, the leakage current increases, which increases the transistor power dissipation, causing even more heat. For this reason the bias circuit must be designed to keep the leakage current to the recommended, safe value.

The base-to-emitter voltage decreases with increasing temperature. A typical temperature coefficient of base-to-emitter voltage is —2.5 millivolts per degree centigrade. Again, the bias circuit design must take this temperature effect into account and provide a base-to-emitter voltage that is in accordance with the expected operating temperature. The technician making repairs on transistorized TV sets must be sure to replace transistors and their circuit components exactly and in the same location to avoid temperature problems.

TRANSISTOR CONNECTIONS

From vacuum-tube circuits we know that at least three different connections of the triode are possible. In ordinary amplifiers the cathode is grounded, the grid forms the input, and the plate is the output. In cathode followers the plate is at a-c ground and the cathode provides the output. For high frequency amplifiers a grounded grid connection with cathode input and plate output is sometimes used. In transistor circuits the three possible connection methods are very important because they provide quite different characteristics.

Figure 4-3 shows the three possible transistor circuits. They are equivalent in circuit, but not in characteristics, to their three vacuum-tube counterparts. The common-emitter circuit (Figure 4-3A) corresponds to a grounded cathode amplifier, except for

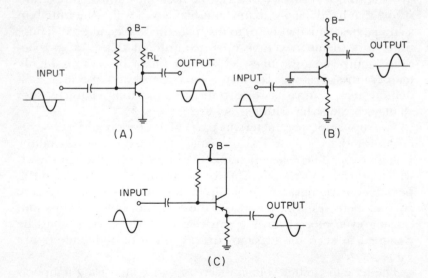

Fig. 4-3. Transistor connections: (A) common emitter circuit; (B) common base circuit; (C) common collector or emitter follower circuit.

input and output impedance. A typical audio transistor, such as the 2N525, will have about 1300 ohms input impedance, 50,000 ohms output impedance, and a power gain of 40 db. Voltage and current gain depend, of course, on the output load, but under optimum conditions the former can be as much as 270 times and the latter 35 times. Just as in its vacuum-tube counterpart, the common emitter circuit inverts the phase of the input signal by 180°.

The common-base connection (Figure 4-3B) corresponds to the grounded grid circuit in vacuum tubes, especially since here, too, the input impedance is very low (35 ohms for the 2N525). Output impedance is 1 megohm, power gain is 26 db, and current gain is less than 1. Only the voltage gain is high, about 380 times. This circuit also inverts the phase of the input signal 180°.

Common-collector or emitter-follower circuit characteristics (Figure 4-3C) are quite similar to those of the cathode follower. High input and low output impedance, 350,000 and 500 ohms, respectively, are coupled with unity voltage gain and a modest power gain of 15 db for such transistors as the 2N525. This circuit is used whenever a high input impedance is needed for matching some other device, such as a phono cartridge. Emitter followers are also used to drive low impedances, such as coaxial cables. The input signal is reproduced at the output with the same phase as at the input, just as it is in a cathode follower.

In vacuum tubes the grid impedance is unaffected by any variation in the plate load or cathode biasing, but transistors do not provide the same isolation between input and output. The collector load resistance is reflected back into the base circuit and will change the base impedance considerably.

Biasing

Biasing, the d-c voltage conditions of the base with respect to collector and emitter, will determine many other characteristics of the entire transistor circuit. Transistors of the same type are not nearly as uniform in their electrical characteristics as vacuum tubes, so a range of values is usually given. Also, as mentioned before, transistors are very temperature-sensitive; the gain, cut-off current, and many other parameters change considerably with temperature. In determining the biasing conditions, all these possible variations must be taken into account. Figure 4-4 shows the input characteristics for the 2N525 at different temperatures. Notice that for 0.15 volts of bias on the base, about 1.75 ma of emitter current will flow at 25°C, which is normal room temperature. At 55°C, a temperature often reached inside a hot chassis, less than 0.1 volt bias produces the same emitter current. In other words, if the bias remains the same, the increase in temperature would increase the emitter current beyond the maximum permissible and this would wreck the transistor. A resistor in the emitter lead itself would limit the emitter current, of course, but the bias would also change.

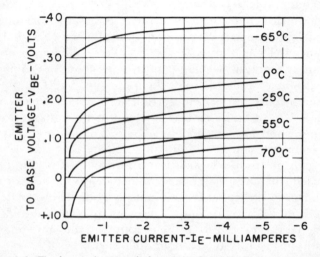

Fig. 4-4. The input characteristics of the 2N525. (General Electric)

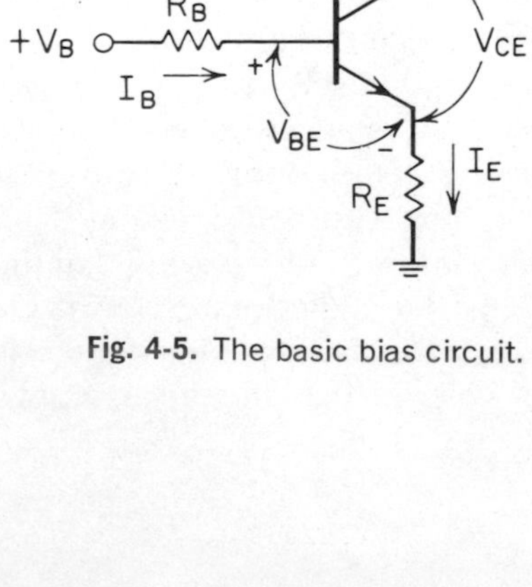

Fig. 4-5. The basic bias circuit.

Figure 4-5 shows the basic bias circuit for a transistor. Although a grounded emitter is shown here, the voltage relations apply for all three types of connections. Note that there are two collector currents, I_C , given. I_{CO} is the small collector current that flows even though the transistor is cut off. This current is quite important for circuit designers and changes considerably with temperature. For the television technician, the important features of biasing are illustrated by the actual biasing circuits shown in Figure 4-6. We can distinguish those circuits that feed a portion of the signal at the collector back to the base. This negative feedback always reduces the gain, but it also increases circuit stability somewhat because excessive increase in collector current increases the bias.

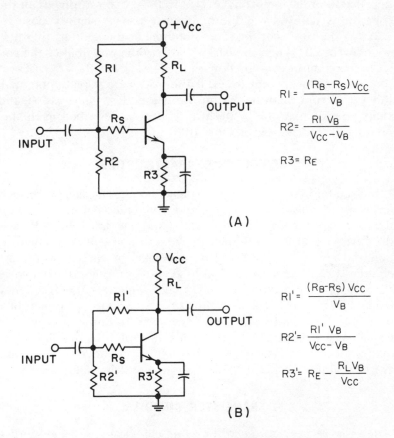

$$RI = \frac{(R_B - R_S) V_{CC}}{V_B}$$

$$R2 = \frac{RI \ V_B}{V_{CC} - V_B}$$

$$R3 = R_E$$

(A)

$$RI' = \frac{(R_B - R_S) V_{CC}}{V_B}$$

$$R2' = \frac{RI' \ V_B}{V_{CC} - V_B}$$

$$R3' = R_E - \frac{R_L V_B}{V_{CC}}$$

(B)

Fig. 4-6. Typical bias circuits: (A) voltage divider; (B) with feedback.

An advantage gained with the voltage-divider bias circuit is that it fixes the d-c potential of the base firmly and makes it less subject to variations of the output current. On the other hand, it also reduces the input impedance of the circuit and attenuates some of the input signal. Inclusion of the emitter bias resistor is optional in any type of circuit.

Forward Biasing. Whichever biasing circuit is used, and regardless of whether the transistor is n-p-n or p-n-p, remember that the base must be "forward-biased" with respect to the emitter; i.e., the base voltage must be between the voltage of the emitter and collector. In a p-n-p circuit the collector is negative with respect to the emitter and therefore the base must also be at least slightly negative in order to permit current to flow. In an n-p-n circuit the collector is positive and the base must also be slightly positive.

When the base is at the same potential as the emitter, the transistor is cut off. When the base is close to the potential of the collector, maximum current flows and we say that the transistor is *in saturation*. In vacuum tubes, if the grid were at plate potential, this would ruin the tube, but in transistors this is permissible and simply means that one of the two diodes, as described in the beginning of this chapter, is shorted.

TRANSISTOR CHARACTERISTICS

In vacuum-tube technology, we have become familiar with such terms as *transconductance,* or g_m, and other tube parameters. Two parameters often used are the *alpha* and the *beta* values. Beta is the current gain for a-c signals in the common-emitter configuration and alpha is the ratio of the a-c collector current to the a-c emitter current in the common-base configuration. Of particular significance is the alpha cut-off, which indicates the frequency limitations of the particular transistor. Similar to vacuum tubes, transistors are limited in their frequency response by their internal construction. Their gain drops off rapidly as the alpha cut-off frequency is reached. That frequency is defined as the point at which alpha reaches 0.707 of its low frequency value.

TRANSISTOR CIRCUITS

Transistors are subject to the same electrical laws as any other circuit element and all of the electronic theory that applies to amplifiers, oscillators, detectors, mixers, and so forth, applies equally

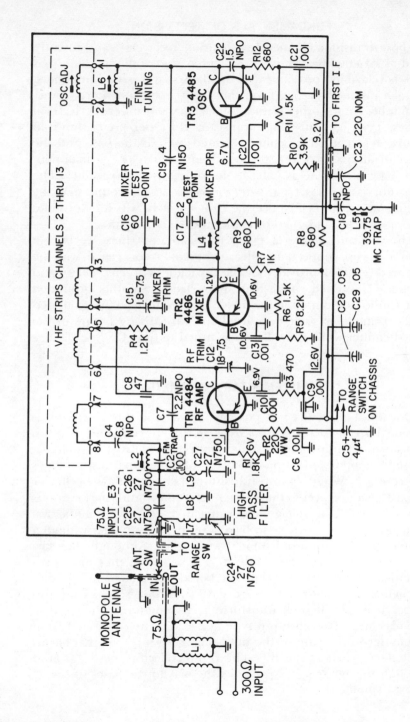

Fig. 4-7. A vhf transistor tuner circuit. (Motorola)

to those transistor circuits. In television receivers transistors are used as r-f amplifiers, mixers, i-f, video, and audio amplifiers, as well as relaxation oscillators, r-f oscillators, and power amplifiers. In each instance they perform the same circuit function as a vacuum tube, but the other elements usually are of different electrical values. Typical of this is the transistor vhf tuner circuit shown in Figure 4-7. The r-f amplifier is tuned both at the base and the collector and is used in a grounded emitter circuit. A small neutralizing capacitor helps stabilize the collector-base reactance. The transistor is a p-n-p type, with the collector at ground and the emitter at +6.9 volts. Notice the range switch, which determines the forward bias and, therefore, the gain of the amplifier.

The oscillator is also a p-n-p transistor, but here we have a grounded base connection, at least where r-f is concerned, with the required feedback provided by the capacitor between collector and emitter. The tuned circuit is in the collector. Another grounded base connection is used in the mixer stage, similar to the grounded grid r-f amplifier sometimes used for vhf. Mixing occurs in the tuned emitter while the collector is tuned to the i-f.

COMPLEMENTARY SYMMETRY

One of the circuits not possible in vacuum-tube receivers is called the *complementary-symmetry amplifier*. It combines a p-n-p and an n-p-n transistor in a d-c connection. This is possible because both input and output polarities of these two transistor types are reversed. While a p-n-p transistor operates with the collector negative with respect to the emitter, its n-p-n counterpart requires a positive collector voltage and a negative emitter. In audio systems this makes it possible to have a push-pull amplifier without a centertapped output and input transformer. Although such circuits are found less frequently in TV receivers, they are worth investigating. Figure 4-8 shows a keyed agc system using complementary symmetry. The agc gate transistor receives positive pulses from the flyback transformer. Its emitter has a negative agc bias on it. It is an n-p-n type and is directly connected from its emitter to the base of the next stage, a p-n-p type that has its emitter returned to the B+. The p-n-p collector goes to ground through the agc bus and provides the bias to the bases of the i-f and r-f amplifiers.

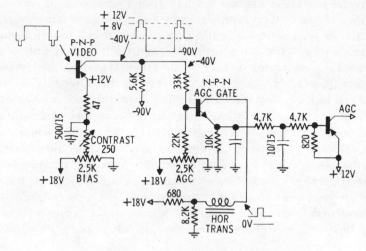

Fig. 4-8. A transistor keyed agc circuit.

Complementary symmetry usually requires that both transistors have the same operating characteristics unless negative feedback or some other control voltages are applied. Because transistor tolerances are usually fairly wide and matched complementary pairs are relatively expensive, complementary-symmetry circuits are not found very often in television sets.

As each stage of the television receiver is analyzed in the following chapters, both vacuum-tube and transistor circuits that perform the particular circuit functions will be discussed. The important features to remember about transistor circuits are the relative impedances, the difference between p-n-p and n-p-n, the characteristics of each type of circuit, the importance of biasing, and the meaning of the transistor parameters. Keeping these features in mind, we can usually analyze a transistor circuit in terms of its equivalent triode, substituting base for grid, emitter for cathode, and collector for plate.

SERVICING TRANSISTORS

Just as tubes are numbered for type identification, so has each transistor type a separate number. All diode numbers start with 1N..., while transistors start with 2N... or 3N.... Most of the latter are special types having a fourth element, somewhat like the tetrode, but these are not usually found in television receivers. Unlike the tube type number, the transistor number does not indicate any characteristic, except that between two identical numbers the one having the suffix A is generally a later and sometimes a slightly better version of the other. It is therefore possible to substitute a 2N...-A for a 2N..., but not the other way around.

Transistors are produced in a number of different ways and are mounted in several different can sizes. Some typical transistors are shown in Figure 4-9. Transistors capable of dissipating more than 0.5 watts are usually larger and have the collector connected to the case for best heat dissipation. These power transistors are often operated with a *heat sink,* a black metal mounting which helps radiate heat away from the transistor. In some cases the transistor is insulated from the heat sink by a mica wafer, while sometimes the heat sink is anodized aluminum, which is its own insulation.

Fig. 4-9. Some representative transistors

Occasionally, the heat sink is insulated from the chassis. Never operate a power transistor without its designated heat sink, except for just a few seconds in a test.

Heat is a great enemy of transistors and can destroy them even when they are not electrically connected. Since transistors are often soldered directly into the printed circuit board, great care must be taken not to apply too much heat to the leads or the case when replacing them. Either clamp long-nosed pliers between the solder joint and the case or else use alligator clips with wet felt between the jaws to carry away the heat of the soldering iron. Another occasional trouble source is soldering irons that have a-c line voltage leakage to the soldering tip. The high voltage can exceed the transistor breakdown voltage and wreck it. For this reason manufacturers use only low-voltage, transformer-driven soldering irons for transistor work.

Testing transistors with an ohmmeter on the higher resistance scales is also dangerous because the voltage thus applied can damage the transistor. In general, transistors can safely withstand voltages up to 10 or 12 volts, although some types are designed for as much as 90 volts. In all cases it is advisable to follow the TV set manufacturer's instructions carefully before testing or replacing any transistor. Since they are much more reliable than tubes it is not necessary to suspect them first as the defective component in any particular malfunctioning circuit.

Test Equipment for Transistors

A variety of transistor testers are available commercially and the technician expecting to do a considerable amount of transistor work will find it worthwhile to invest in such an instrument. Transistor tests usually can measure whether a transistor is open or shorted and can determine the beta, or current gain. Just as with tube testers, pin connections and voltages must be looked up on a chart and the readings of gain checked with that chart. Even the less expensive testers are usually satisfactory.

Ohmmeter tests can be made to determine open or shorted transistors by connecting the base first to the collector and measuring the resistance between collector and emitter. (A p-n-p transistor must be tested by placing the plus lead of the ohmmeter on the collector; an n-p-n type requires reverse polarity.) With the base connected to the collector, the transistor should have relatively low resistance (50 ohms or so for small signal transistors and less than 10 ohms for power types). With the base connected to the emitter, the resistance should increase at least 20 times. Use the second lowest ohmmeter scale to avoid burning out the transistor with too much current or too high a voltage.

Review Questions

1. To which side of a p-n diode must the positive battery side be connected to prevent current flow?
2. Why is the base in a transistor similar to the control grid in a vacuum tube?
3. If input and output voltage in a transistor amplifier are the same, how can this stage have gain?
4. Which transistor circuit has the highest input impedance?
5. With fixed forward bias, what is the effect on the emitter current if the temperature is increased?
6. What is meant by *alpha cut-off frequency?*
7. What is meant by the *beta* of a transistor?
8. What is the difference between p-n-p and n-p-n circuits?
9. Why are power transistors operated with a heat sink?
10. Which transistor connection offers best voltage gain?

COLOR TV FUNDAMENTALS

We know from basic physics that all light is a form of electro-magnetic radiation of very high frequency or very short wave-length which the human eye is capable of receiving and identifying. Different objects reflect the various light frequencies differently and therefore appear to us to be colored. A green object, for example, reflects the green and absorbs all other colors. When white light shines on it, our eyes receive only the reflected energy and see it as green. Color television, like all color reproduction processes, depends on the peculiarities of the human eye, as well as on the fundamentals of color physics, to create the colored image. For this reason, we need to know something about color vision and color physics before we can get a sound understanding of how color TV works.

COLOR VISION

We can compare the human eye to a radio receiver that is peaked at the center of the band and receives signals ranging in wave-length from 0.4 to 0.7 micron (10^{-6} meters). A wavelength of 0.5 micron corresponds to a frequency of 600 million megacycles. The very short wavelengths are often measured in angstrom units, one of which equals 0.00000000397 inch (1 micron is equal to 10,000 Angstroms). Light is obviously a very, very high frequency radiation.

The full range of pure colors of the visible spectrum occurs rarely in nature, but it is visible in rainbows and oil slicks or whenever white light is broken up into all its components. When a light beam is passed through a prism, the full color spectrum appears because each of the different wavelengths of light is refracted differently. The colors of the spectrum are called the *primary* or *saturated colors* because they are pure, individual frequencies. In a typical spectrum, such as that shown in Plate I, the blue and violet colors are at the high frequency end and the reds are at the low frequency side. Below the red portion is the invisible infrared or heat region. The invisible ultraviolet region is above the visible blues. Somewhere in the center of the spectrum is the green region, the color range to which the eye is most sensitive.

Color Brightness. The frequency response of the human eye is shown in Figure 5-1. We can see that the sensitivity curve is very much like that of a radio receiver. If we want blue to appear as bright as green we must have more light power at the blue than at the green. Because *brightness* is such an inexact term, in technical descriptions we must distinguish between the overall brightness of a scene and the amount of light of a particular color. The brightness associated with a color is called *luminance,* whereas in television, brightness refers to the level of the black-and-white, or monochrome, illumination.

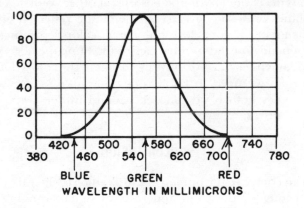

Fig. 5-1. The frequency response curve of the human eye.

Brightness has another important effect in color vision that is best defined by the old saw that "at night all cats are grey." This refers to the fact that at low levels of illumination the human eye cannot distinguish at all between colors. An object that may appear as bright yellow in daylight will appear brownish at dusk and grey at night. This means that the luminance of a color determines the appearance of the color itself. Red cannot appear as green at different light intensities, but fire-engine red will appear as dull or dark red when the luminance or illumination level is reduced, just as white fades to grey and eventually to black. This concept is important for the proper adjustment of color TV receivers.

Color Integration. Another aspect of the human eye is its integrating ability. The eye combines small dot patterns into a single image. When small black dots are grouped close together we see dark grey shading. The same dots, spaced further apart, appear as light grey shading. This can be verified by looking closely at any reproduction of a photograph in this book. All printed half-tones (photographs) are made up of dot patterns that the eye integrates into shades of grey; in darker shades the dots are closer together, in lighter shades they are further apart. This integrating effect also applies to colors. Look closely at any of the color reproductions in this book and you will notice that they are made up of small dots of different colors; e.g., purple areas consist of closely-spaced red and blue dots. The eye combines or integrates these colors to produce another color. This color mixing ability of the human eye makes the present color TV system possible, because the color picture tube really reproduces only a mass of small dots of different colors.

COLOR PHYSICS

We have said that the pure or primary colors visible in the rainbow rarely occur in nature. Since most objects appear in the colors they reflect and since they rarely reflect only one frequency, they present a mixture of frequencies to the human eye. This mixture is interpreted as pastel colors, meaning that some white, or rather some small parts of other colors, is reflected with the predominant primary color. To represent this situation in graphical form the color diagram of Plate II is generally used. This horseshoe diagram is rimmed by the spectral or primary colors which mix to give us the "color" that appears to us as white. The straight line at the bottom represents those shades of purple obtained by mixing only various amounts of red and blue. On the color diagram, lengths correspond to amounts of a particular color when colors are mixed, but this holds strictly true only for transmitted and not for reflected light. As an example, we can shine a red and a blue spotlight on a white object and it will appear to be purple. We can also mix red and blue paint and obtain a purple color. However, if the right amounts of red, green, and blue light are projected on a screen, the total effect will be white, but no combination of paint colors will produce white. Fortunately, this latter condition can be disregarded for color television because we deal here only with transmitted light.

The color diagram of Plate II represents only one particular level of brightness where differences in colors are really differences in hue, not in luminance. In nature, however, we find that objects have many different degrees of brightness or luminance, such as the shadows in a particular scene. To represent this geometrically, we can construct a pyramid of color diagrams, as shown in Plate III. The brightest colors are at the base and the dimmer colors form smaller triangles building towards the apex of the pyramid, a black spot that represents the point of zero illumination or absolute darkness. The center, the white portion of the diagram of Plate II, represents the center of the pyramid and tapers from bright white through grey until it ends in the black spot at the apex.

Using the Color Pyramid

To specify a particular color within the pyramid, we can use the three primary colors and give their distance from the black spot at the pyramid's apex. This means that we use the three luminance values of R, G, and B that are mixed to make the final color. Another way of specifying the same color would be to use the distance of the particular color diagram from the apex of the pyramid, and specify two hues in that particular color diagram. The relation between any of these dimensions is geometrically determined and corresponds mathematically to actual color values. The mathematical principles involved play a vital role in the method of transmitting color TV signals from transmitter to receiver. For color TV these values are shown in Figure 5-2.

Returning to the color diagram of Plate II, we see that if we select points in three of the primary colors (red, green, and blue) and connect them by drawing a triangle, different mixes of these three colors in different combinations will produce a large range of colors lying inside the triangle. That is exactly what is done in color TV and in some other color reproduction processes. It is true that by this method we cannot reproduce all possible colors, but, just as in high fidelity sound, the reproduction is so close to the original that the human eye cannot usually distinguish the difference. Combinations of the three primary colors chosen for television produce practically all of the colors normally seen. Only when we try to re-

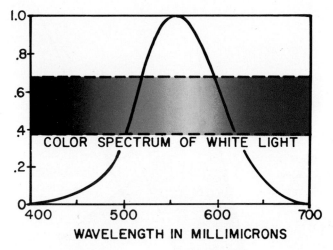

Plate I. The color spectrum.

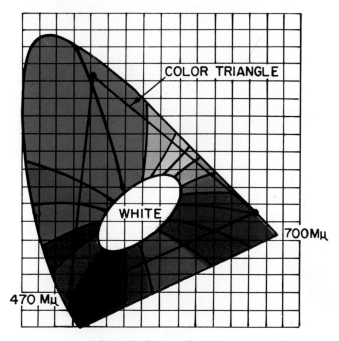

Plate II. A color diagram.

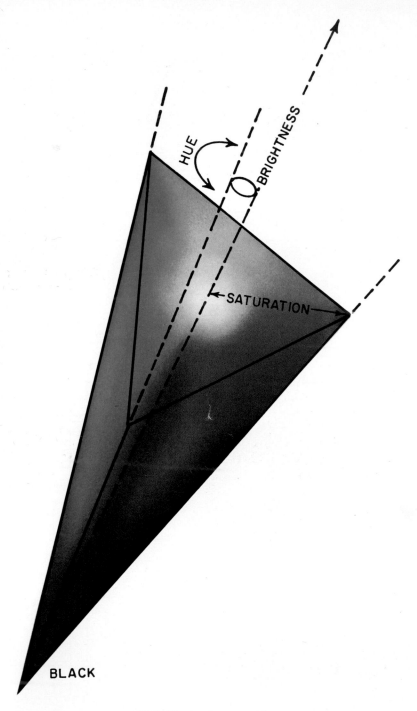

Plate III. A color pyramid.

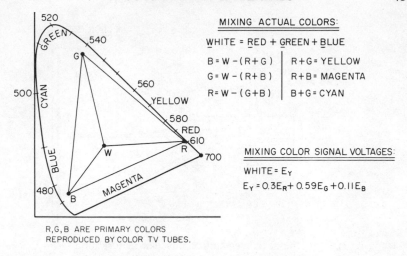

MIXING ACTUAL COLORS:

WHITE = RED + GREEN + BLUE

$B = W - (R + G)$	$R + G = YELLOW$
$G = W - (R + B)$	$R + B = MAGENTA$
$R = W - (G + B)$	$B + G = CYAN$

MIXING COLOR SIGNAL VOLTAGES:

WHITE = E_Y

$E_Y = 0.3E_R + 0.59E_G + 0.11E_B$

R,G,B ARE PRIMARY COLORS
REPRODUCED BY COLOR TV TUBES.

Fig. 5-2. Color signal relationships.

produce such effects as sunlight shining through green leaves, or the colors of an open fire, is there any detectable difference between nature and the electronic reproduction.

COLOR PICTURE TUBE PRINCIPLES

A color picture can be produced by shining three projectors on a screen, each showing only one of the picture's three primary colors—red, blue, or green. Early systems used three cathode-ray tubes, one for each primary color, and combined their images with a special set of mirrors. Present color sets, however, use a single picture tube that has a screen containing dots of phosphor which glow in the three colors. Figure 5-3 shows the arrangement of elements in the tricolor picture tube. The primary colors are mixed by the integrating action of the eye, which combines the individual colored dots into an area of mixed color, in the same fashion that it integrates the red and blue dots in the printed color picture cited earlier.

As shown in Figure 5-3, there are three separate electron guns. Each gun produces its own electron beam and is aimed at only those phosphor dots corresponding to its respective color. Each gun contains a heated cathode, control grid, and first anode, but focusing is accomplished for all three by a common electrostatic focusing element. The second anode is also common to all three electron guns. Two special elements are used here to assure that

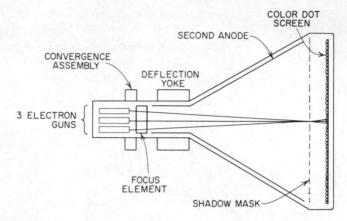

Fig. 5-3. The basic elements of the color picture tube.

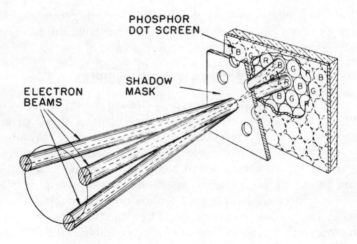

Fig. 5-4. The shadow mask and color screen. (RCA)

each electron beam strikes only its respective color dots. The *convergence element* controls the positioning of the electron beams and the *shadow mask* acts like a sieve to let only those electrons through that will strike the correct color dots.

Figure 5-4 shows, in greatly enlarged form, how the three electron beams pass through the shadow mask holes to illuminate a particular set of three color dots. The luminance of each color is determined by the respective color video signal modulating the control grid of each electron gun. Thus, during a purely red portion of the picture, the electron beams of the blue and green guns are shut off and only the red phosphor dots are illuminated. When purple is displayed, only the red and blue guns get through, and when white shows on the screen all three electron beams are turned on to the carefully balanced amount of luminance which combines the three primary colors to give the eye the impression of white.

Additional elements and special circuits are required in the color picture-tube section of a color receiver to assure that the colors are uniform over the entire screen, that focus is maintained, and that the proper color balance is achieved. Chapter 15 is devoted to color picture tubes and their circuits. At this time, only the fundamentals are required for an understanding of the color TV system.

COLOR SIGNALS

From the preceding discussion of color picture tubes, we know that three separate video signals are required to drive the picture tube. These three signals must correspond to the video signals obtained from the three color camera tubes, each of which "sees" one of the primary colors. Thus, when the color camera "looks" at a red portion, the green and blue camera tubes will be cut off; and a purple portion or spot will cause the green tube to be turned off. The video output signals of each of the three camera tubes cannot be transmitted directly, because this would require three television channels for just one color picture. To conserve frequencies and remain within the existing black-and-white television channel assignments, an ingenious method of coding the color information has been adopted.

Phase Modulation

Stripped of its mathematical and highly theoretical background, this method of color transmission can be understood if we consider two separate principles: *phase modulation* and *frequency interleaving*. Amplitude modulation, AM, is used in broadcast radio and for black-and-white TV video signals. It simply means that the *amplitude* of the r-f carrier is varied. Frequency modulation, FM, is used in broadcasting and for the television sound and means that the *frequency* of the r-f carrier is varied. (More details concerning the color signals are presented in Chapter 16.) Phase modulation, the third possible means of modulating a carrier, means that the carrier's phase is changed instead of its amplitude or frequency. In order to detect phase modulation, however, we must know what the reference, or unmodulated, phase should be. Then we can take the difference between the reference and the received phase and obtain the transmitted information (in this case, the color video signal) as this phase difference. Figure 5-5 illustrates the subtraction of reference and transmitted phase of a single cycle of a sine wave, both as it would appear on the oscilloscope and as it is represented by vectors. (The following discussion involves simple vector analysis, a mathematical procedure that is used to represent phase relationships. A complete understanding of this aspect of color TV is not essential to color receiver servicing.)

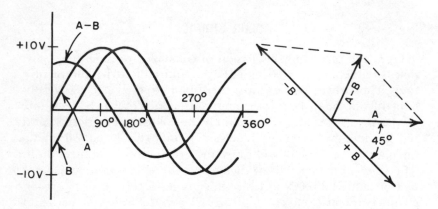

Fig. 5-5. Subtracting two sine waves.

We have shown how any point in the color pyramid can be described by either the three primary color values, including hue and luminance for each, or by giving the brightness or *Y level* and then specifying the hues only of two of the primary colors. The latter method is used in color television. The Y or brightness parameter is transmitted as the regular black-and-white video signal while the remaining two hue values are transmitted as phase modulation. The three video signals from the triple color camera are converted into the brightness and hue signals at the transmitter. At the receiver these signals are converted back into the RGB signals that drive the color picture tube. The circuits which perform the color signal conversion are treated in Chapter 16.

Figure 5-6 shows the phase relationship between the transmitted reference phase and the various color or chroma signals. We can

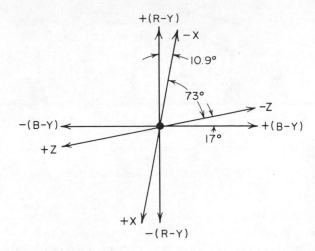

Fig. 5-6. The vector diagram of the color-difference signals.

think of this vector diagram in terms of the color diagram where the white center corresponds to the origin of the vector diagram and the vector angle corresponds to hue. Amplitude of the chroma signal would then correspond to distance from the white center. This is not a true correspondence but may help those unfamiliar with vectors to understand how chroma information is transmitted.

We have spoken of phase difference of the color signals, but have said nothing about the frequency of these signals. The color signals modulate the phase of a sine wave of 3.58 mc, which is called the *color subcarrier*. The reason for this name will become apparent when we consider the second principle of color transmission, *frequency interleaving*.

Frequency Interleaving

Both theoretical analysis and spectrum analyzer studies reveal that the regular monochrome video signal, extending from 30 cps to about 4 mc, is not a continuous band of frequencies. This means that electromagnetic energy is not present at every cycle between 30 cps and 4 mc. Because the lowest repetitive frequency is the 30-cps vertical scanning rate, the energy in the video frequency spectrum consists of narrow strips spaced 30 cps apart and clustered about the horizontal 15,750 cps harmonics, as shown in the simplified spectrum chart of Figure 5-7. Once this characteristic of the monochrome video signal is understood, it will become obvious

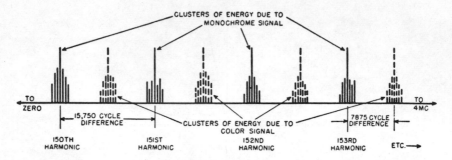

Fig. 5-7. A simplified spectrum chart.

that any color signal that also contains the same scanning rates will
have the same characteristic. All that is necessary now to complete
the picture is to use a color subcarrier, phase modulated with the
hue signals, which is based on a 15,750 cps rate that is 7875 cps
higher or lower than the monochrome signal. The two signals, the
monochrome and the color subcarrier, can then be interleaved and
fitted into the same 4-mc bandwidth. In actual practice, the color
subcarrier frequency is 3.579545 mc, and fits exactly into the correct slots between the monochrome signal's intervals.

In the frequency spectrum chart of Figure 5-8, we note that the
color subcarrier does not have equal bandwidth above and below
the reference point. This is justified by the fact that the human eye
is not equally sensitive to all colors. We know that the eye is less
sensitive towards the blue portion of the spectrum and cannot recognize as much fine detail there as it can at the green and yellow

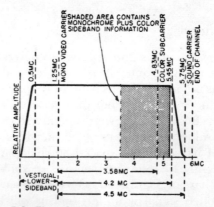

Fig. 5-8. The r-f spectrum of a color TV channel.

portions. For this reason, not as much bandwidth is needed at the blue hues. Referring back to the color vector diagram of Figure 5-6, we note that in additon to the $R-Y$ and $B-Y$ signals we also show the X and Z vectors. Each of these represents a color element that lies somewhere between the red, blue, and green primary colors on the triangle superimposed on the color diagram. These vectors are chosen for convenience in demodulating and matrixing at the receiver; theoretically, any other two vectors could be used. More details concerning this feature are presented in Chapter 16.

The complete r-f transmission spectrum of a typical color channel is shown in Figure 5-8. Note that the overall frequency distribution is the same as for a monochrome channel except for the color subcarrier. This is why it is possible for a monochrome set to receive a color transmission and display it in black and white; all that is missing is a means to demodulate the color subcarrier and reproduce the color portion. This also means that a color set will contain all of the functions of a monochrome receiver, plus circuits to demodulate and display the color information.

COLOR SYNCHRONIZATION

Phase modulation, as we have already noted, requires that the phase-modulated carrier be compared with a reference signal. In the case of the color subcarrier, we must have a 3.579545-mc sine wave with the exact zero phase so that we can electronically compare it cycle by cycle with the chroma signal and demodulate the actual hue values. At the transmitter, this reference signal is used to encode the color information; at the receiver we must have an

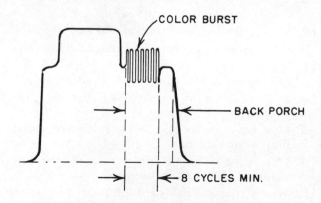

Fig. 5-9. The color sync burst.

exact duplicate of this reference signal to decode the color information. This means that another signal must be transmitted. This is accomplished by using the pedestals of the horizontal synchronizing pulses, as shown in Figure 5-9, and amplitude modulating that portion with eight cycles of the reference signal. At the receiver we find a local oscillator, running at approximately 3.579545 mc, which is synchronized with the color sync burst at the start of each horizontal line. As long as this oscillator is correctly synchronized, it will reproduce the exact reference signal at the receiver that enables the color demodulator section to compare the color subcarrier against it. Chapter 17 is devoted to the circuits used to generate the color sync signal from the eight-cycle burst riding on each horizontal pedestal.

Review Questions

1. Which color light has a higher frequency, yellow or blue?
2. What is the meaning of *luminance?*
3. What color is at the center of the color diagram?
4. What color lies at the apex of the color pyramid?
5. Name the primary colors used in television.
6. Which two elements of the color picture tube determine that each electron beam strikes only its correct color dots?
7. How is the color information modulated on the subcarrier?
8. What is the purpose of the 3.58-mc burst sent out on each horizontal blanking pedestal?
9. What information is transmitted as Y signal?
10. What information is transmitted as X and Z signals?
11. What principle permits transmission of all signals for color TV within a single 6-mc channel?
12. What is the approximate overall bandwidth of the color subcarrier sidebands?
13. How many cycles of 3.58-mc reference signal are transmitted for each line?
14. How is the screen of a color picture tube different from that of a black and white type?
15. Which characteristic of the human eye is utilized in the color picture tube?

TV RECEIVER FUNCTIONS

As we have learned in Chapters 2 and 5, television signals are transmitted from the station over a channel that is 6 megacycles wide and there are a total of 82 such channels assigned in the U.S. The black-and-white picture information is transmitted by amplitude modulation, the sound uses frequency modulation, and the color, where used, depends on phase modulation of the color sub-carrier. Because all of these signals are contained in a single, 6 mc-wide channel, all of the r-f and i-f functions associated with broadcast or communications heterodyne receivers can be common to the three main signals. As illustrated in Figure 6-1, the basic functional elements of such a receiver consist of the antenna, the r-f tuner, the i-f amplifier, and the detector.

Beyond the detector, the various signals must be treated differently. The sound, being frequency modulated, must be detected by an FM detector and amplified by an audio amplifier before it

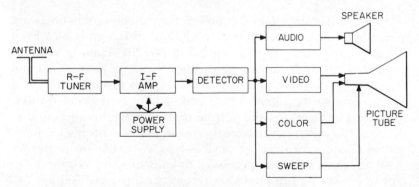

Fig. 6-1. The basic functional elements of a television receiver.

can drive the loudspeaker. The video signal, containing the mono-chrome picture detail, must be amplified by a video amplifier be-fore it is applied to the picture tube. The vertical and horizontal synchronizing information must be extracted from the composite video signal in order to lock in the vertical and horizontal sweep sections. Color information must be separately treated to obtain the final color video signals. The power supply furnishes the re-quired d-c voltages to all other receiver sections.

All essential black-and-white TV receiver functions are shown in the block diagram of Figure 6-2, which will be used as a reference for most of the discussion in this chapter. (Color functions are treated at the end of the chapter.)

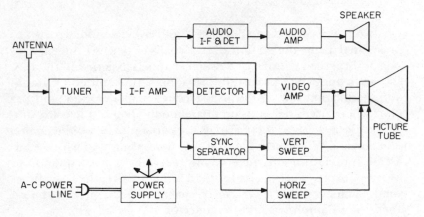

Fig. 6-2. The basic black and white TV receiver functions.

ANTENNA

We have mentioned in Chapter 2 that television channels are generally grouped into the low, high, and ultrahigh bands. Even the low band, from 54 to 88 mc, is in the vhf region and trans-mission is mostly by line-of-sight, since these frequencies are not reflected by the ionosphere. For best TV pictures it is essential that a fairly strong signal is obtained without reflections or inter-ference. The need for this will be more thoroughly discussed in detail in Chapter 14, which treats antennas and transmission lines, and in Chapter 21, which describes typical installation problems.

At this time, it is only necessary to know that the built-in loop-type antennas used in broadcast receivers cannot be used for TV. In general, a much more complex antenna is required, either built-in, indoor, or outdoor. Because of the different frequency bands, a single antenna cannot cover all 82 channels, although in strong signal locations the mismatch and losses may not seem to matter. Most sets receiving only the vhf bands, 54–88 mc and 147–217 mc, channels 2–13, will use an antenna arrangement that is tuned to both bands. For uhf reception, a separate antenna is usually required, but because of the shorter wavelengths this antenna can be much smaller.

Together with a special antenna, TV receivers also use a special transmission line to bring the signals to the tuner with minimal loss, reflection, and noise. The most common type of transmission line is a flat, ribbon-like, twin lead with a characteristic impedance of 300 ohms. For best impedance matching, the antenna, as well as the tuner input, should have the same impedance. 300 ohms is the standard value for all TV sets. The flat 300-ohm line is not quite as effective for uhf, which requires a special, hollow, twin lead.

TUNER

From the antenna, the transmission line brings all received signals to the tuner, which has the job of selecting the desired band of frequencies and rejecting all others. The tuner contains the basic elements of any heterodyne front end. It contains a tuned r-f amplifier, a local oscillator, a mixer, and tuned circuits that pass only the desired intermediate frequency to the i-f amplifiers. In TV tuners the most complex portion is the actual tuning mechanism. In order to cover the frequency range of TV channels, the tuner must be capable of tuning from 54 to 890 mc but skip several ranges (72-76, 88-174, and 216-470 mc). As continuous tuning has not proven very practical, TV tuners use channel switching, at least for the vhf channels. Most tuners cover only the vhf portion with a separate, additional tuner used to cover the uhf band.

I-F AMPLIFIER

Television i-f amplifiers differ from those used in radio receivers in that their bandwidth is much greater and their frequency response is not really symmetrical. These requirements mean that a number of stages, usually about three, are used to amplify the i-f signals. Earlier receivers used an i-f of 21.25 to 25.5 mc, but since about 1956 all receivers use an i-f of 41.25 to 45.5 mc. In the newer receivers, both sound and video signals are amplified together; in color sets the 3.58-mc color subcarrier is also amplified along with the brightness and sound signals. To prevent overloading and to minimize picture changes during fading, automatic gain control is used to control the amplification of the i-f signal. This bias voltage is applied to at least two of the i-f amplifiers and care is taken to avoid changing the frequency response curve as agc bias changes.

VIDEO DETECTOR

A simple diode detector is used to remove the amplitude-modulated video signal from the i-f. At the same time, the sound carrier, which is 4.5 mc removed from the video carrier signal, appears as a 4.5-mc, frequency-modulated signal. In color sets, the color subcarrier appears as a phase-modulated, 3.58-mc signal mixed in with the monochrome or brightness signal. The video detector circuit sometimes includes a tuned network to trap out the 4.5-mc sound signal, but in many sets both sound and color subcarriers are amplified along with the brightness signal in the first video amplifier stage.

VIDEO AMPLIFIER

The function of the video amplifier is similar to that of the audio output amplifier that drives the loudspeaker, but the video or brightness signal contains much more detail and therefore requires more bandwidth. Generally speaking, video amplifiers have a bandpass of about 3.5 to 4 mc, which is achieved by using special peaking circuits for the high and low frequency response. In color sets the color subcarrier presents no interference because of the frequency interleaving, as explained in Chapter 5.

The video amplifier section amplifies the picture signal from less than a volt, available at the detector, to the 50 to 90 volts required to drive the picture tube. Another function of the video amplifier is to drive the picture tube with the correct polarity of video signal. (This section is covered in Chapter 11.)

AUDIO I-F AND DETECTOR

The 4.5-mc second sound i-f signal is removed from the detector or the first video amplifier stage by a sharply tuned circuit and is then amplified, clipped, and limited like any FM signal. The detector is either a discriminator, ratio detector, or shaped beam-tube type of detector. Detailed circuits will be discussed in Chapter 17.

AUDIO AMPLIFIER

The TV audio amplifier is identical to the audio amplifiers found in radio receivers and any other audio equipment.

SYNC SEPARATOR

The sync separator is unique to television receivers. From Chapter 2 we know that the horizontal and vertical sync pulses appear on top of their respective blanking signals, which are sandwiched in between lines of picture signal and extend into the "blacker-than-black" region. In the sync separator section, the sync pulses are clipped off the composite video signal after this signal has been amplified by the video amplifier. To separate the vertical from the horizontal sync pulses, two separate filters are used. A high pass filter permits only the horizontal pulses to reach the horizontal sweep section while the vertical pulses are passed through a low pass filter to the vertical sweep section.

VERTICAL SWEEP SECTION

In the vertical sweep section a free running oscillator generates the 60-cps sawtooth current that will pass through the deflection yoke and move the electron beam up and down. To keep the picture from rolling up or down, this sawtooth generator is synchronized to the frequency of the vertical sync pulses coming in from the sync separator. The sawtooth signals are then amplified sufficiently. Usually a dual triode, or three transistors, performs both sawtooth generation and amplification, as will be shown in more detail in Chapter 7.

HORIZONTAL SWEEP SECTION (FLYBACK)

Because horizontal sweep signals are more critical than vertical sweep signals, the horizontal sweep section is much more elaborate than its vertical counterpart. Synchronizing the horizontal signals with the sync pulses requires quite a tricky circuit and amplifying these short sawtooth waves is quite difficult. In order to obtain the large current of very short duration required in the horizontal deflection coils, a transformer is generally used between the output amplifier and the deflection yoke. The inductance of the deflection coils and transformer causes the short, steep retrace portion of the sawtooth signal to overshoot and oscillate. To overcome this a special damping diode is usually used. Because relatively large amounts of energy are used here at a 15,750 cps rate, it is practical to add an autotransformer winding to the horizontal output transformer and step the signal up to a high voltage. This high voltage is then rectified and filtered and serves as second anode potential for the picture tube. The high voltage is generated during the time the electron beam returns from right to left, which is why this action is referred to as *flyback* and we speak of the *flyback transformer* as part of the horizontal sweep section. Since this particular receiver section is a source of frequent defects and is quite different from circuits encountered in radio or audio work, a detailed description of it is found in Chapter 8.

POWER SUPPLY

In television receivers the power supply can become much more complex than in radios because larger currents and higher voltages are needed. Most television power supplies use transformers and at least full-wave rectifiers, as well as more complex filters and voltage-divider networks. Power supply circuits differ according to the type of receiver. Color TV sets have the largest and most critical power supply, while small-screen portables require less power and simpler filtering.

SPECIAL COLOR TV CIRCUITS

The television receiver sections discussed so far are essential in every type of set, whether it is a transistor portable or a color set, but the color sets require some additional circuitry. All color receivers contain circuits for synchronizing the color demodulator to the 3.58-mc reference burst, for demodulating the color subcarrier itself, and for resurrecting the three color signals from the demodulated subcarrier. Finally, the color picture tube requires special circuits to paint a distortion-free color picture.

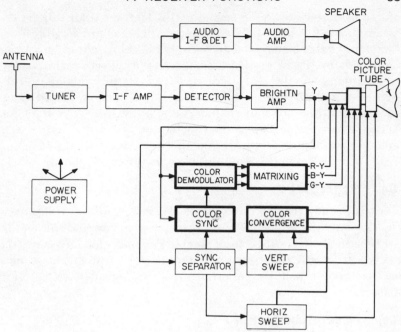

Fig. 6-3. The color television receiver functions.

Color Synchronizing Section

Figure 6-3 shows the block diagram of a typical color set with the special sections required for color emphasized by heavy borders. Note that the color sync section obtains its signals from the sync separator and from the horizontal sync section. We know from Chapter 5 that the color sync burst perches on the blanking pedestal of each horizontal sync and blanking pulse. This portion is clipped off at the sync separator and, by using a gating signal from the horizontal sweep section, all other signals except the burst are kept from reaching the color sync oscillator. This 3.58-mc sine-wave oscillator is locked into the exact phase of the reference burst and then, through phase-shifting networks, the proper reference phase is supplied to the color demodulator section.

Color Demodulator

To get from the video detector, or first video amplifier, to the final three color signals requires a number of separate steps. First the composite video signal, including the 3.58-mc color subcarrier, is amplified by the bandpass amplifier. This eliminates the low-frequency video signals and allows only the color subcarrier and its sidebands to reach the demodulator section. Two separate color demodulator circuits are used, each with a different phase reference signal, to phase detect the two hue vectors, X and Z, as explained in the previous chapter. (The phase-detector circuit deserves considerable explanation—Chapter 16 is devoted to the color demodulator action.) From the demodulated X and Z signals we must next obtain the three color difference signals.

Color Matrix Section

At the color picture tube, the $R-Y$, $B-Y$, and $G-Y$ difference signals must be applied with the proper polarity and amplitude to be added in the tube itself to the Y signal. The color matrix section contains the necessary amplifiers, resistive matrix networks, and, usually, some adjustments to permit correct color balance.

Color Picture Tube Section

We already know what controls, voltages, and circuits are necessary for the monochrome picture tube, but the color tube is much more complex, adjustments are much more critical, and a number of additional voltages and signals are needed. Because of the color dot arrangement and the need to keep all three electron beams focused only on their respective color dots, signals are needed to provide this correction voltage both for the vertical and horizontal sweep. Usually a separate deck or chassis is used that contains only the controls needed to keep the electron beams properly converged. In addition to the second anode voltage, high voltage is also used to provide electrostatic focus for all three electron guns. As we can see, a number of special circuits are required for the color picture tube. They are described in detail in Chapter 15.

When reading the following chapters, it is important to keep the overall television receiver block diagram and the functions of the different sections in mind, because they all work together. Failure in any one section will affect the set's performance. When troubleshooting receiver defects, an understanding of these receiver functions is essential to isolate defects to a particular section and then to a particular stage. Without this methodical approach, TV troubleshooting becomes a time-consuming, haphazard search instead of a planned, efficient, and profitable business.

Review Questions

1. How is the sound carrier modulated?
2. What is the sound carrier frequency if the video is 175.25 mc?
3. What is the standard TV antenna and transmission line impedance?
4. Name the three basic tuner functions.
5. What is the usual range of frequencies of video i-f?
6. What important signal frequencies appear at the detector output of a color set?
7. What is the order of amplification expected in the video amplifier?
8. How does the sync separator remove sync pulses from the composite video signal?
9. During which part of the horizontal scan does the high voltage pulse occur?
10. To what is the color sync oscillator synchronized?
11. How are the X and Z video signals obtained in the color receiver?
12. What function has the color matrix section?

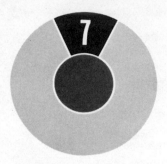

MAGNETIC DEFLECTION
AND THE VERTICAL SWEEP SECTION

We have learned in Chapters 2 and 3 that the picture is "painted" by the electron beam, which traces out the entire raster on the screen of the picture tube. The motion of the electron beam is controlled by magnetic fields that are generated by external deflection coils and pass through the glass envelope. To sweep the beam from side to side the horizontal deflection coils are used, but to generate the entire raster, a much slower vertical magnetic force must be applied to move the beam downward while individual lines are traced out. The vertical sweep occurs at the rate of 60 times a second and the horizontal sweep is at the 15,750 cps line frequency. In this chapter we will describe the method of producing the vertical, 60-cps sweep; first, however, the principles of magnetic deflection must be considered.

MAGNETIC DEFLECTION

The interaction between magnetic lines of force and the flow of electrons in a wire makes transformers, motors, and generators possible. It applies equally to a stream of electrons moving in a vacuum; e.g., the electron beam inside the TV picture tube. These principles concern the direction of electron motion at right angles to the direction of magnetic lines of flux, following the "right-hand rule." Figure 7-1 shows two cross sections of the picture tube neck with the electron beam coming out of the page toward the reader. Note that magnetic lines of flux "flowing" horizontally across the path of the electron beam deflect that beam either up or down, depending on the direction of the flux lines or the polarity of the magnets creating them.

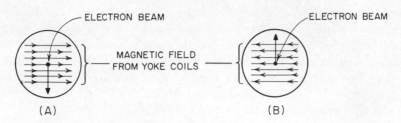

Fig. 7-1. Magnetic flux and the electron beam: (A) beam deflected down; (B) beam deflected up.

In television, two identical flat coils are placed on either side of the electron beam and the current through them is controlled. To move the electron beam down during the "painting" portion of the picture, a relatively slow, but linear, sawtooth current is passed through the two coils. When the beam is at the bottom of the screen, the polarity of the current is reversed quickly to deflect the beam to the top of the screen. This quick reversal takes place during the *retrace* period when the picture tube is blanked out. To get an idea of how this waveform is generated, consider the pulse generator of Figure 7-2, which drives an RC network. During the long positive portion of the rectangular wave, the capacitor charges slowly, causing the voltage across the load resistor to increase gradually. When the generator suddenly reverses polarity, the capacitor discharges, causing the downward slope in the voltage wave. The value of the resistor and capacitor, as well as the internal impedance of the pulse generator, must be carefully chosen so that the charging and discharging portion of the sawtooth wave is relatively linear. If the wrong values are used, the charging time may extend into the dotted portion of the curve of Figure 7-2, which is not linear.

The time period for which the capacitor and its resistor load are reasonably linear is a short part of the RC constant, which is the

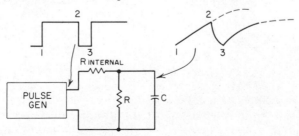

Fig. 7-2. RC charging.

mathematical product of capacitance and resistance, usually expressed in microseconds. The internal resistance of the generator determines the charging time and the load resistor is effective during the discharge period. For this reason the internal resistance must be much greater, since the charging time, corresponding to the "painting" time, is much longer than the discharging time, which corresponds to the retrace period.

One more concept must be understood before we can consider actual circuits. We have stated that the magnetic deflection action depends on the current through the coils, which must have the sawtooth waveform shown in Figure 7-2. Since the deflection coils are an inductance, together with some inherent resistance, the current and voltage will be different. If the sawtooth voltage obtained in Figure 7-2 is applied across a resistive load, a sawtooth current will flow as indicated in Figure 7-3C. To get a sawtooth current to flow in a pure inductance, the pulse voltage waveform of Figure 7-3B would have to be applied across the coil. Since practical deflection coils contain both inductance and resistance, the combination voltage of Figure 7-3C is applied to the coils to produce the sawtooth current and, therefore, the sawtooth magnetic field.

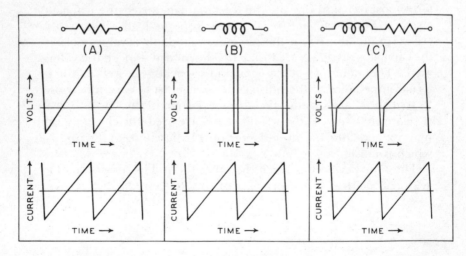

Fig. 7-3. Voltage and current waveforms.

The principles of magnetic interaction with tne electron beam, the charging and discharging of the RC network, and the voltage and current waveforms required should all be kept in mind when you are studying the actual deflection circuits.

RELAXATION OSCILLATORS

The reader should be familiar with sine-wave oscillators from audio and radio work. Their operation depends on feedback and their frequency is determined by a tuned circuit. Relaxation oscillators also use feedback but their frequency is controlled by the charging and discharging time of RC networks. We know from Figure 7-2 that the desired output waveform from the relaxation oscillator should be unsymmetrical to provide for the longer "painting" time of the electron beam and the much shorter retrace period. Such waveforms are generated by two basic types of circuits: the *multivibrator* and the *blocking oscillator*. Both types are found, with various modifications, in television receivers, and a brief explanation of basic circuits is in order before actual receiver circuits are discussed.

Multivibrator

The basic multivibrator of Figure 7-4 provides the feedback through C1 and C2. When power is first turned on one of the capacitors will charge heavily. Let us assume, in this case, that C1 charges through R4 and R1, making the grid of V1 positive, which increases the plate current in V1. As this plate current increases, the plate becomes more negative. This negative-going plate voltage of V1 is impressed through C2 on the grid of V2 and that tube rapidly goes into cut-off, making the plate of V2 as positive as the B+. When C1 is charged and V1 is conducting fully, a momentary state of equilibrium exists. V1 conducts and V2 is cut-off. At this

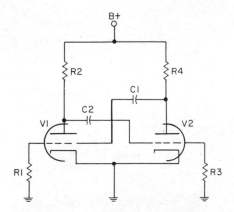

Fig. 7-4. The basic multivibrator circuit.

time, C2, which has been discharging through R3, loses enough charge to start current flowing in V2, driving the V2 plate voltage negatively. This negative-going voltage goes through C1 and drives the grid of V1 more negative, causing V1 plate current to be reduced and making the V1 plate more positive. Again, the increase in positive-going voltage reduces the charge on C2, increasing the plate current of V2. Now V2 is going into full conduction while V1 is going rapidly towards cut-off. After a state of equilibrium is reached, C1, which has been discharging through R1, loses enough charge to start current flowing in V1 and the cycle begins all over again. If R1 and R3, R2 and R4, C1 and C2 are equal values in each pair, the resultant voltage at either plate will be a square wave. In television receivers we need an unsymmetrical wave shape to account for "painting" and retrace time and therefore choose unequal values for C1, C2, and the resistances. Figure 7-5 shows the waveforms at the different points of a typical multivibrator as used in TV.

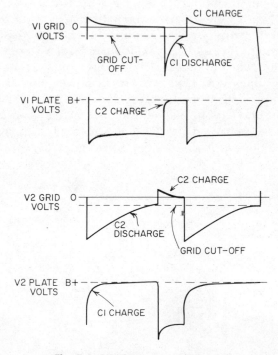

Fig. 7-5. Multivibrator waveforms.

Blocking Oscillator

In the blocking oscillator, the feedback is provided by transformer coupling and only a single triode stage is required. Figure 7-6 illustrates the basic circuit together with the voltage waveforms at the plate and grid. As B+ is applied, C2 is charged through R2 and the plate voltage and current rise. This rise in plate current is coupled through the transformer so that the grid voltage, through C1, also becomes more positive. As this feedback action rapidly builds up the plate current to the saturation level, increases in grid voltage no longer increase the plate current and the transformer's field starts to collapse. Now, a negative-going potential is coupled to the grid, driving the tube rapidly towards cut-off. At point *c* on the grid voltage waveform, the tube is cut-off again and plate current stops flowing. As C1 slowly discharges through R1 and R3, the grid goes more positive, but only when point *e*, the cut-off value, is reached, can plate current start to flow again. As this occurs, the transformer builds up a field and the cycle starts again.

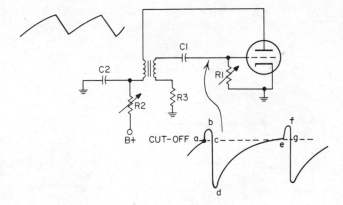

Fig. 7-6. The blocking oscillator circuit.

Note that in this system the tube is cut-off during the longer period and conducts only during the short interval that corresponds to the retrace time. The voltage across C2 will have a sawtooth waveform because the tube acts as low impedance during the conducting period, discharging C2, while during the cut-off period the tube is a high impedance, allowing current through R2 to charge C2. The "painting" time is determined here by the values of R1, R3, and C1, while the retrace time is a function of the tube,

C2, and the transformer. R2 also enters into the retrace time, but primarily affects the amplitude of the sawtooth waveform across C2. We shall see in actual circuits that R1 and R2 are potentiometers controlling the frequency and the amplitude, respectively.

We have seen that both the multivibrator and the blocking oscillator are free running, meaning that they oscillate continuously by themselves. In TV receivers we must synchronize them to the vertical or horizontal sync pulses. This can be done only when their free-running frequency is very close to that of the sync pulses. Then, if the sync pulse appears at the respective grid just before the circuit is ready to change, it will accomplish the change and sync the oscillator correctly.

TYPICAL VERTICAL SWEEP OSCILLATORS

Actual circuits found in TV receivers differ slightly from the elementary examples shown in Figures 7-4 and 7-6, but their operation is the same. The vertical oscillator shown in Figure 7-7 is a typical multivibrator circuit. It differs from the basic circuit of Figure 7-4 only in that the first grid does not receive the feedback

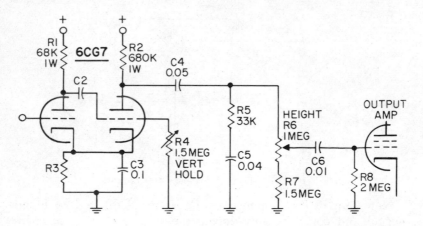

Fig. 7-7. A typical multivibrator circuit.

signal. Instead, both cathodes are connected together and have a common resistor going to ground; this cathode coupling provides the necessary feedback action. Note that the two plate resistors differ by a factor of 10:1, a ratio which determines the difference between the painting and retrace time portions of the multivibrator signal output. The repetition rate is determined by the grid resistance consisting of the vertical hold potentiometer and its series resistor. The height or amplitude of the output signal is determined by the amount of signal coupled from the plate of the second multivibrator stage to the output amplifier. To generate the combination sawtooth and pulse voltage waveform required to produce a sawtooth current in the deflection yoke (Figure 7-3), the output of the multivibrator goes to the RC network R5 and C5. The values of these two components are chosen to give the desired voltage waveform for a 60-cps signal.

The typical blocking oscillator circuit shown in Figure 7-8 will usually be found in older sets. Here, the oscillator and output amplifier are a single dual triode. The entire circuit will be analyzed.

As in the basic circuit of Figure 7-6, the plate of the oscillator is transformer-coupled to the grid and the repetition frequency is controlled by the grid bias resistor, in this case R1, in series with R2, which limits the range of R1. The vertical sync signal is applied to the grid through the transformer and acts to hasten the instant of positive-going grid. The cut-off period is determined by the time it takes C1 to charge up through the integrating network, which is part of the sync separator circuit and is not shown in this diagram.

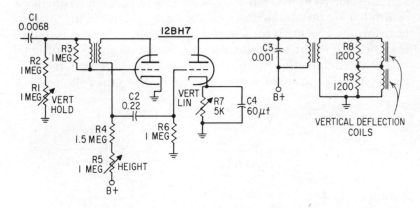

Fig. 7-8. A typical blocking oscillator circuit.

To generate the desired combination sawtooth and pulse signal the values of C2 and R6 are chosen so that the output amplifier can operate as a linear triode stage. The height of the vertical sawtooth is determined by the potentiometer R5, which controls the B+ to the blocking oscillator stage. It is apparent from the circuit that this control will also affect the linearity of the sawtooth to some extent because it affects the charging time of C2. To compensate for any nonlinearity in the sawtooth signal on the grid of the output amplifier, the cathode bias resistor is a potentiometer which controls the gain and linearity of that stage. In actual receivers a compromise setting between all three controls, vertical hold, height, and linearity, must be achieved since each of them affects somewhat the action of the others.

Note that the output amplifier of Figure 7-8 is transformer-coupled to the vertical deflection coils. These coils are low impedance and the transformer is a means of matching their impedance to that of the triode plate circuit. The small capacitor C3 improves the response of the transformer during the short retrace period. (The output portion of the vertical sweep section is treated with more detail later.)

A Transistor Blocking Oscillator

A transistor version of the blocking oscillator circuit just described is shown in Figure 7-9. (This circuit is used in the *Motorola Astronaut* portable TV set.) The blocking oscillator stage is almost an exact analog of the triode circuit of Figure 7-8 because the base and collector go to the transformer and the repetition frequency is controlled by the RC network in the base return circuit. A third transformer winding is used here to couple the vertical sync pulses into the base of the transistor. Height, or size, of the output signal is controlled with the emitter potentiometer. Note that the sawtooth charging capacitor network is driven from the collector. For

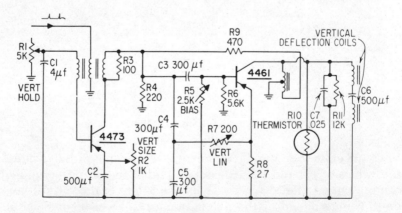

Fig. 7-9. A transistor vertical sweep section. (Motorola)

better linearity, a portion of the vertical transformer output signal is coupled back to the oscillator collector. The output amplifier is a medium-power transistor with adjustments for base bias and emitter degeneration for linearity control.

Component values are quite different from those used in vacuum-tube circuits because impedance and voltage requirements are so different. Note that the base charging capacitor, C1, is 4 μfd as compared to C1 in Figure 7-8, which is .0068 μfd. Coupling and bypass capacitors are similarly larger, while resistance values are much lower. The output transformer and the deflection yoke are functionally the same as their vacuum-tube circuit equivalents, but their actual values are quite different. Because p-n-p transistors are used, the collectors must be negative with respect to the emitters. In this particular circuit the emitters are at a positive potential while the collectors go to ground. The vertical deflection coils are separated by a capacitor that prevents the power-supply current from flowing through them. Additional RC networks are included to improve the deflection linearity and suppress ringing or damped oscillations.

A Modified Multivibrator Circuit

In most of the recent TV receivers a modified multivibrator circuit is used that combines the output amplifier with the first stage of the multivibrator. This saves the cost of the blocking oscillator transformer and also eliminates the need for the extra triode stage required in the older multivibrator and output amplifier arrangements. This saves one triode, as is shown in the circuit of Figure 7-10. The right half of the 6DE7 double triode acts as output amplifier, driving an autotransformer that feeds the vertical deflection yoke windings. The multivibrator action is obtained through connections from each of the triode plates to the grids of the other tube, just as in Figure 7-4. The main difference is that in Figure 7-4 this was accomplished by the coupling capacitors C1 and C2, while in the modified multivibrator circuit a whole network consisting of C6, R8, C8, R10, R11, and C9 shapes the feedback signal from the output stage to the first stage. This is necessary because the voltage at the plate of the output stage has to appear like the voltage waveform in Figure 7-3 in order to produce a good sawtooth current in the deflection yoke. Note that in the multivibrator of Figure 7-4 the two cathodes were connected to ground together, while in Figure 7-10 a common d-c path exists between the two grids.

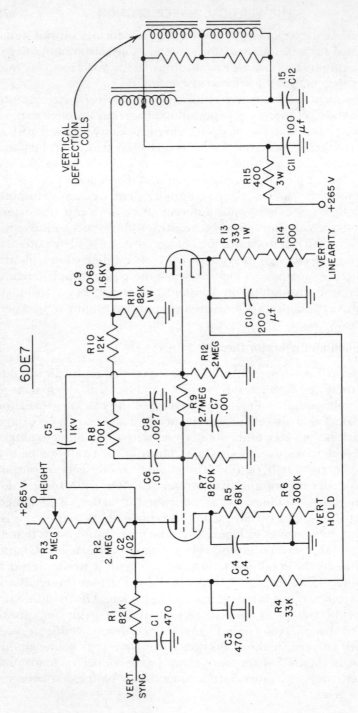

Fig. 7-10. The circuit diagram of the vertical oscillator and output amplifier.

Vertical synchronizing pulses are applied to the plate of the first stage and the grid of the second stage through the coupling capacitor C5. A feedback signal from the cathode of the output stage to the plate of the first stage serves to improve the linearity of the sawtooth signal. By varying the plate voltage on the first stage, the amplitude of the oscillations and, therefore, the height of the picture are regulated. Varying the cathode bias on the first stage sets the approximate frequency and adjusts the vertical hold. Changing cathode bias in the output stage affects the vertical linearity just as in the output amplifier of Figure 7-8.

OUTPUT AMPLIFIER

In place of the regular transformer used to match impedances between the deflection coils and the output stage, many recent sets use an autotransformer similar to that in the circuit of Figure 7-10. To keep the vertical sweep signal from the rest of the TV receiver, power-supply bus isolating resistor R15 and capacitor C11 are used. This effectively a-c grounds the tap on the autotransformer and C12 is then across the secondary portion of the autotransformer, serving the same speed-up function for the retrace time as C3 did in Figure 7-8.

It is a universal practice to connect small resistors across each of the vertical deflection coils in order to reduce the Q of these coils and limit any damped oscillations or "ringing" due to the rapid change in current direction. The transistor circuit of Figure 7-9 uses an RC network for the same purpose. In some TV sets these resistors are in series with a *thermistor*. This is a special resistor which changes its resistance with temperature. It is mounted with the damping resistors inside the deflection coil assembly so that when that component becomes hot the thermistor also gets hot. As heat increases, the resistance of the deflection coils increases and reduces the current through it. The picture height shrinks, too. The thermistor, connected across the coils, increases also in resistance, reducing its shunting effect and thereby compensating for the increase in coil resistance. In transistor circuits a thermistor is almost always used as illustrated in Figure 7-9. Here, the thermistor is not located at the deflection yoke but is connected across it. The important thing for the technician to remember is that when replacing the thermistor, an exact duplicate having the same temperature characteristics must be used.

Although in the examples so far we have shown only triodes as vertical output stages, many sets, especially those made before 1960, use pentodes. The principles of circuit operation and all of the controls are invariably the same.

ADJUSTMENT AND TROUBLESHOOTING

Adjustment. All vertical sweep circuits have three potentiometers, as shown in the preceding examples. Because they interact with each other, a definite adjustment procedure should be followed to save time and do a professional adjustment job. First, set the vertical-hold control so that the picture rolls slowly from bottom to top and finally just snaps in. Next, adjust the height control until the picture fills the screen vertically and overlaps slightly beyond the edges of the escutcheon. If the picture starts to roll during this adjustment, reset the vertical hold control. Next, observe the spacing of the horizontal lines at the top, bottom, and center of the screen and check the appearance of round objects. Adjust the vertical linearity control to compensate for compression or expansion at top or bottom and reset the height control once more.

When it appears that good vertical linearity with sufficient height is obtained, adjust the hold control to roll the picture slowly from bottom to top and observe the spacing of horizontal lines as the picture moves. If necessary, touch up the height and linearity controls once more, then set the hold control until the picture snaps in firmly. Check for correct hold adjustment by switching channels to determine that the picture appears locked-in at once without first rolling a few seconds.

Troubleshooting. Troubleshooting the vertical sweep section is relatively simple because its defects usually show clear symptoms. If the picture tube shows only a horizontal line, then the vertical sweep is missing. This can be due either to a defect in the oscillator or in the amplifier, or, least likely, in the deflection coils. Signal tracing can be done either with an oscilloscope or with earphones, since the 60-cps signal is clearly audible. Loss of synchronization must be due either to a loss of sync pulses, which points to the sync separator section, or to a defective component in the oscillator circuit. The latter defect can be found with simple ohmmeter checks. Presence of sync pulses can be checked by the oscilloscope if the oscillator tube is first removed so that its signals can't obscure the sync pulses.

Vertical nonlinearity that cannot be adjusted can invariably be traced to a defective component such as a leaky capacitor or a gassy tube.

Troubleshooting transistor vertical deflection sections is based on the same principles of signal tracing and component testing as for tube circuits, except that transistors are less likely to become defective than are their vacuum-tube counterparts.

Review Questions

1. In which plane must the magnetic field lie to move the electron beam up and down?
2. How is a pulse voltage changed into a sawtooth voltage?
3. What will be the current waveform in an inductance when a pulse voltage is applied across it?
4. How many transistors or triodes are used in a multivibrator?
5. What are the two equilibrium conditions of a multivibrator?
6. What kind of components determine the multivibrator frequency?
7. How many transistors or triodes are used in a blocking oscillator?
8. Which capacitor in Figure 7-6 determines the retrace time?
9. Which components in Figure 7-7 determine the difference between painting and retrace time?
10. Which components in Figure 7-7 determine the combination sawtooth and pulse voltage?
11. Why does the setting of the height control in Figure 7-8 affect vertical linearity?
12. Why are the RC values in a transistor blocking oscillator so much different from a vacuum-tube circuit?
13. List two feedback capacitors in the circuit of Figure 7-10.
14. What is the function of the resistors connected across each deflection coil?
15. How is loss of vertical sweep apparent on the screen?

THE HORIZONTAL SWEEP SECTION

The requirements of the horizontal sweep in television receivers are quite severe compared to those of the vertical sweep. Not only is the frequency much higher (15,750 cps), but the synchronization of the sweep with the transmitted sync pulses must be absolutely perfect. The vertical sweep was synchronized at 60 cps, which is the power-line frequency and errors of a few microseconds do not matter. In the horizontal scanning, however, even half a microsecond error between successive lines will give a severe picture distortion. To obtain this accuracy, the horizontal sweep section necessarily contains more circuitry than its vertical counterpart and, therefore, usually is the most troublesome portion of the TV set.

In this chapter we will discuss the horizontal oscillator and how it is synchronized, the output amplifier, flyback transformer, and deflection coils, and the necessary damping circuit. There are a number of other receiver sections that depend on signals from the horizontal sweep section; their features will be discussed in connection with those other receiver sections.

PRINCIPLES OF AUTOMATIC FREQUENCY CONTROL

All television receivers, black and white as well as color sets, use some means to automatically check and readjust the horizontal oscillator frequency. These automatic control circuits operate by comparing the sync pulses with the output of the oscillator and then controlling the oscillator frequency accordingly. The basic

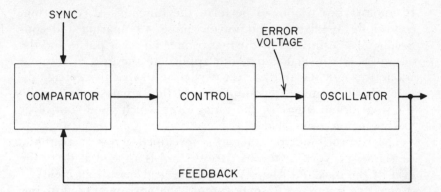

Fig. 8-1. A block diagram of the basic afc system.

block diagram of Figure 8-1 illustrates the essential parts of this automatic frequency control (afc). Sometimes the comparator and control circuit are contained in a single stage, but their functions are separated into the comparing and controlling operations.

The oscillator can be any of the relaxation types discussed in Chapter 7, but usually a blocking oscillator type is used. To improve the ease of frequency control, the oscillator usually contains some sine-wave action so that the output is not exactly the combination sawtooth and pulse desired, but a combination sine-wave pulse that is changed into the desired waveform in a later circuit.

Comparing the sync pulse with a pulse fed back from the oscillator requires either two diodes or two elements of a triode. The circuit is designed to allow the two signals to cancel each other when they are exactly in step with each other, which means they are of the same frequency and phase. When the oscillator is faster or slower than the sync pulses, either a positive or negative output signal is generated which then controls the oscillator by either slowing it down or speeding it up until it is again exactly in step with the sync pulses. In the following analysis of typical circuits, we shall see exactly how the comparing, controlling, and feedback elements operate.

SYNCHROGUIDE

Probably the most widely used horizontal afc system is the *Synchroguide* developed by RCA. With minor modifications this circuit will be found in over 50% of all receivers made before 1962 and in many later sets as well. This circuit is shown in Figure 8-2.

It employs two triodes to perform the functions of comparing, controlling, oscillation, and waveforming. Comparing and controlling are performed by the first triode. The sync pulses and the output of the oscillator are both applied to the grid of the first triode through R1 and C1. C2 is part of a capacitive voltage divider that determines the amplitude of the signals applied to the triode grid and, thereby, the range over which good control or locking action is obtained.

The control or error voltage is developed across the cathode resistance network of the first triode and is applied as dc to the grid of the oscillator stage. Varying the grid bias of an oscillator controls its frequency to some extent. The horizontal hold or frequency control, a manual touch-up adjustment, is simply a potentiometer in the plate circuit of the control triode that determines the tube current and, therefore, the cathode voltage. During the painting time, the first triode is cut-off and conducts only during the positive sync pulse period. When this pulse coincides with the positive peaks of the feedback signal, the conduction time is very short and little current flows in the control tube. When the sawtooth signal frequency is higher, when it occurs before the sync pulse, or lower, when it occurs after the sync pulse, the conduction period is either longer or shorter than when correct sync exists and the positive cathode bias either increases or decreases accordingly.

The oscillator itself varies in different receivers between one that contains coupling between grid and cathode and a circuit that couples between grid and plate. In either type, an additional tuned circuit, L1 and C7 in Figure 8-2, is used in series with either the plate or cathode to provide sine-wave ringing. This stabilizes the oscillator frequency over several cycles, even though the error voltage varies. When adjusting the horizontal hold control, it will be noticed that the sync action takes a second or so, a delay that is due to the flywheel effect of the sine-wave component. The horizontal hold adjustment described above is a vernier setting. Actually, the horizontal frequency is determined mainly by the setting of the two coils on the transformer.

We mentioned that the output of this circuit is not exactly the right wave shape for linear magnetic deflection. Shaping of the wave is done by the RC network coupling the signal from the oscillator to the output amplifier and by the grid leak bias action of that stage.

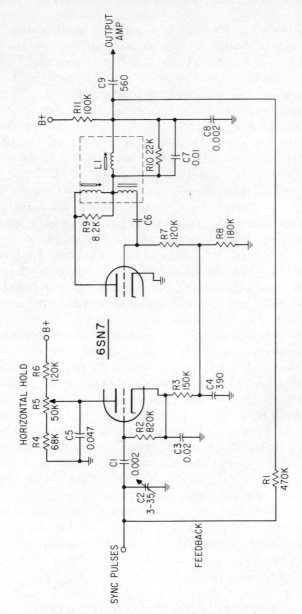

Fig. 8-2. The basic Synchroguide circuit. (RCA)

PHASE DETECTOR AND STABILIZED MULTIVIBRATOR

Most of the recent TV receiver models use another type of automatic frequency control circuit that essentially is a multivibrator, controlled directly by a double-diode phase detector. Figure 8-3 shows the essential circuit elements. CR1 is a double diode, usually either a special selenium or germanium assembly, with the incoming horizontal sync pulse applied to 'the center and the feedback sweep signal applied to one side. When both signals are in correct synchronization, the positive sync pulse occurs just as the retrace portion of the sweep signal rises. The resultant d-c voltage to the oscillator is then at a fixed value, say 1 volt. If the sync pulse coincides with the positive portion of the sawtooth, meaning that the oscillator is too slow, the control voltage will become more positive. When the sync pulse occurs before the start of the retrace period, the control voltage will be more negative. This control voltage is filtered by C3, R3 and C4, and is then applied to the grid of the first triode. In the circuit shown, the feedback sawtooth is obtained from a winding on the horizontal output transformer. One side of that winding goes to ground, providing the ground return for the first triode grid.

The horizontal oscillator is essentially a multivibrator, similar to the one shown in Figure 7-7 and explained in Chapter 7. Here, a tuned circuit, L1 and C5, is inserted in the plate load of the first triode to stabilize the multivibrator and make the afc bias control more effective. This resonant circuit is tuned approximately to the 15,750-cps horizontal sweep frequency and the fine adjustment is made by setting the second triode grid resistance, R8, which determines the RC time constant of C6, R7, and R8 and, therefore, the discharge time. The second triode section also acts as a wave-shaping tube since it drives the RC network consisting of R9 and C8 to change the pulse-type signal into the combination pulse and sawtooth waveform that is necessary to give a good sawtooth current in the deflection coils. Note that in this circuit there is no control that determines the amplitude and, therefore, the width of the horizontal sweep. In most sets the width control is part of the output amplifier.

TRANSISTORIZED HORIZONTAL SWEEP

In transistor TV receivers the horizontal sweep section usually requires more transistors than its vacuum-tube equivalent. This

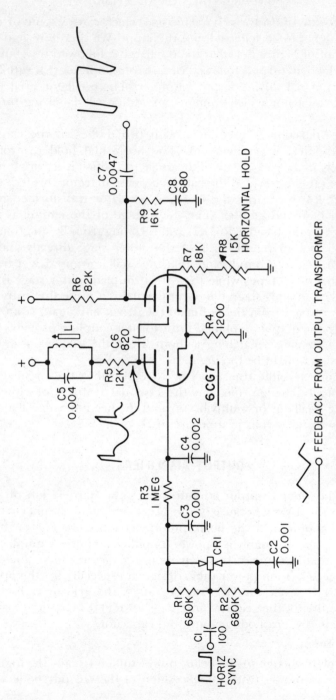

Fig. 8-3. The stabilized multivibrator and phase detector.

C7
0.0047

R9
16K

C8
680

R7
18K

R8
15K
HORIZONTAL HOLD

R6
82K

L1

C6
820

R4
1200

C5
0.004

R5
12K

6CG7

C4
0.002

R3
1 MEG

C3
0.001

CR1

C2
0.001

R1
680K

R2
680K

C1
100

HORIZ
SYNC

FEEDBACK FROM OUTPUT TRANSFORMER

is due to the transistor's characteristic, which causes some of the output signal to be reflected into the input. We therefore find, in the circuit of Figure 8-4, that the oscillator is followed by a buffer stage, which, in turn, is followed by a driver amplifier that supplies sufficient signal to the output amplifier. The oscillator itself is a blocking oscillator which contains an additional stabilizing tuned circuit.

Phase detection is used here with two diodes in the classic, balanced-detector arrangement. The horizontal hold control is effectively in the base circuit of the oscillator, which is accomplished by setting the d-c level of the balanced phase detector through R2, R3, and R4. Note that the blocking oscillator transformer goes between base and emitter. The d-c voltage of the emitter is determined by the bleeder R6, R7, and R8 going from B+ to ground. The collector drives the base of the buffer stage directly and is also returned to ground. Note that the oscillator and driver transistors are p-n-p types while the direct-coupled buffer stage is an n-p-n type. At this stage the output signal is a pulse that is transformer-coupled from the buffer to the driver and again from the driver to the output amplifier. Transformer coupling provides the proper impedance matching without which the loss of power between stages might be too great.

As more versatile transistors become available, the circuits will undoubtedly change, too, but the essential features of either a blocking oscillator or multivibrator and the need for afc will apply in transistor as well as in tube circuits.

OUTPUT AMPLIFIERS

The horizontal output amplifier does the hardest job of any stage in the TV set because of the large current and rapid current reversal required in the horizontal deflection coils. For this reason this stage invariably is a power amplifier that uses a number of special circuit features. In receivers using vacuum tubes the output stage is a beam power tube, designed especially for this application. To handle the large signal range, the grid or cathode is biased either by the grid-leak method shown in the circuit of Figure 8-5 or else by a cathode resistor and capacitor.

Output Tubes

The plate voltage of the beam power tube is usually the highest available in the set (with the exception of the second-anode volt-

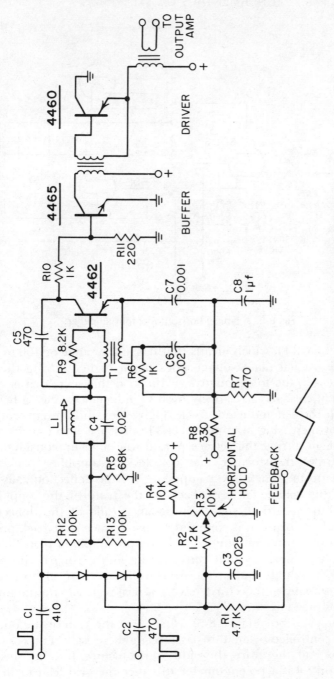

Fig. 8-4. The transistor blocking oscillator and afc. (Motorola)

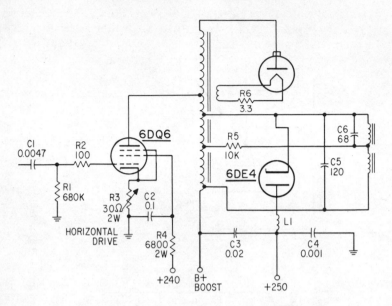

Fig. 8-5. A typical horizontal output amplifier.

age of the CRT), which means that it is in the range of 400 to 600 volts dc. Actual plate voltage goes much higher during the retrace period due to the nature of the load this stage drives. The deflection coils are a relatively high Q inductance; once a field is built up the self inductance will oppose any sudden current reversal by increasing in impedance. This flywheel effect means that the voltage during the retrace period will build up considerably. The output transformer that couples the amplifier plate impedance to the much lower impedance of the deflection coils will reflect this voltage increase back to the plate of the amplifier, stepped-up according to the impedance ratio of the deflection coils and the plate. It is common to find retrace or flyback pulses of 7000 volts peak amplitude on the output amplifier plate. These high voltage pulses would cause arcing and corona if the plate lead were brought out at the tube socket. Almost all horizontal output amplifiers, therefore, have a special plate cap on the top of the glass tube envelope.

In the circuit of Figure 8-5, we see that the gain of the output stage is controlled by an unbypassed cathode resistor. This controls the drive and, therefore, the width of the picture. In other sets the width control is a potentiometer in either the grid lead or in the screen grid supply. In this latter position a 3- or 5-watt potentiometer is used because most amplifiers take considerable screen grid power. Typical d-c currents in the horizontal output amplifier tube range up to about 100 ma for the cathodes and up to 20 ma for the screen grid.

Figure 8-5 also illustrates another feature used almost universally in horizontal output amplifiers: the parasitic suppression resistor, R2, in series with the grid. This resistor helps prevent parasitic oscillations due to the momentarily positive grid current and also reduces the chance for Barkhausen oscillations. This latter phenomenon is very rare in modern TV sets, but was occasionally found in earlier amplifier tubes. It is due to a resonance inside the tube structure that small resistors in the grid and screen grid sometimes help eliminate. Changing the tube is the simplest cure.

Output Transistors

In transistor horizontal output amplifiers, the low impedance of the deflection coils presents an entirely different problem. The circuit of Figure 8-6 shows the output amplifier stage connected as emitter follower, which means a very low impedance in a power transistor. This impedance is so low, a few ohms probably, that the transformer has to step the voltage up. Even then the two horizontal coils are used in parallel instead of in series, as in the vacuum-tube version. The entire output amplifier section is designed for maximum current and, therefore, low impedance.

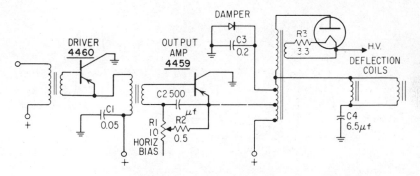

Fig. 8-6. A transistor output amplifier.

We have seen in Figure 8-4 that a buffer stage is included after the oscillator to drive the driver amplifier, which is an emitter follower, and that a step-down transformer is then used to furnish enough current to drive the base of the output amplifier.

R1 sets the bias on the output amplifier base and, to some extent, determines the gain as well as the linearity of that stage. While other transistor output amplifiers may use slightly different circuits, the principle that current rather than voltage is amplified is always found in transistor circuits.

DAMPING

In both Figures 8-5 and 8-6, we have shown a diode connected across a portion of the output transformer. This is an essential feature of all horizontal output sections. We mentioned the flywheel effect before and explained how it causes the build-up of a large positive pulse during the retrace period. This pulse is used to obtain the high voltage, as will be discussed in detail in the next chapter. At the end of this pulse the current through the deflection coils has been reversed and must stop so that the slower build-up that will sweep the electron beam across the screen during the "paint" period can start. The flywheel effect also opposes the sudden stopping of the flyback pulse and, if no special measures are taken, the current will continue to flow, as shown in the sketch of Figure 8-7 by the dotted line. This "ringing" would cause vertical wavy lines at the left side of the screen and would tend to compress the picture at that point. To eliminate it, a diode is connected across the deflection yoke or a suitable portion of the output transformer, as shown in Figures 8-5 and 8-6.

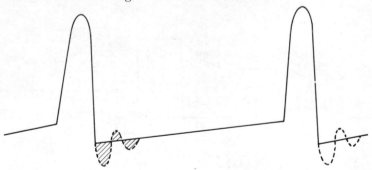

Fig. 8-7. The horizontal deflection voltage waveshape.

Examining Figure 8-5, we see that the cathode of the damping diode will become negative during the "ringing" portion and will cause the diode to conduct. L1, C3, and C4 are a filter. With the plate of the damping diode always at the B+ voltage, C3 will charge up during the diode conduction period so that the low end of the output transformer is at a voltage higher than the B+. This is commonly called the *boost voltage* and can range as high as 700 volts in some receivers. It represents the energy shown in the shaded portion of the waveform of Figure 8-7 and is used at various points in the TV set where high voltage is required. In most sets the charging tube of the vertical sweep circuit and the first or focusing anode of the picture tube use the B+ boost voltage. Many older TV models use damping tubes that have their filaments connected to special "floating" windings on the power transformer, thereby eliminating the danger of cathode-to-filament shorts. Present-day damper tubes are designed with sufficient internal insulation to permit grounding the filaments.

In the transistor circuit of Figure 8-6, the damping diode is a semiconductor connected to ground with C3 acting as the filter. No B+ boost is utilized from the damping diode, but the positive flyback pulses are used for the high voltage as always.

DEFLECTION YOKES

The output transformer used in the horizontal sweep section is quite different from audio or power transformers.* The deflection coils must produce a magnetic field that varies linearly as the electron beam "paints" the picture and is uniform over the entire screen. This means that the physical shape and mounting of the coils themselves is quite critical.

As shown in Figure 8-8, two sets of coils are used, the inner set for the horizontal sweep and the outer set for the vertical deflection. These coils contain ferrite cores that are mounted in a ring around them. The entire assembly is generally called the *deflection yoke* and must be carefully oriented on the neck of the picture tube. To get maximum efficiency the yoke is pushed as far toward the screen as possible. By rotating it the raster can be tilted.

Deflection yokes are made in different impedances and in different mechanical configurations. The impedance characteristics must be known to match a replacement to the transformer. The mechanical arrangement depends on the type of picture tube on which the yoke is used.

Deflection Angle. Not only is the screen size a means of distinguishing different picture-tube types, but the deflection angle is

---

*A detailed discussion of these flyback transformers follows in the next chapter, together with the high voltage section.

Fig. 8-8. A typical deflection yoke. (RCA)

also an important factor. Because the horizontal sweep is longer and much faster than the vertical sweep, the critical deflection angle referred to is always the horizontal. Figure 8-9 illustrates the meaning of this characteristic. Here, we can also recognize the importance of locating the deflection yoke as far forward on the neck of the picture tube as possible. If it is not far enough forward, the electron beam may hit the glass envelope which contains the

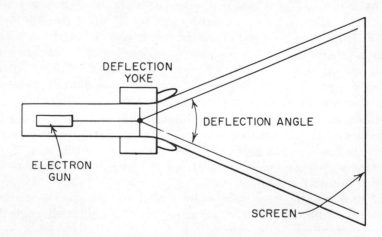

Fig. 8-9. The deflection angle.

second anode coating and thereby cut off a portion of the picture. Deflection angles determine the length of the picture tube and range from about 60° in older types to 110° in the very short-necked picture tubes. To simplify replacement of the deflection yoke be sure that the exact type specified for that particular receiver model is obtained.

ADJUSTMENT AND TROUBLESHOOTING

Defects in the horizontal sweep section can be easily classified into two types: those involving synchronization of the horizontal sweep and those where the sweep signal is either too weak or absent altogether. Loss of synchronization can be due either to loss of the sync pulses, which usually is caused by a defect prior to the horizontal sweep section, or to a defect in the afc system and the horizontal oscillator itself. To make sure that the sync pulses reach the afc circuit, remove the oscillator tube and look for the sync pulses with the scope at the afc circuit. If the defect is in the afc circuit, it will usually be possible to synchronize the oscillator for a moment with the hold control and the frequency adjustment. If the defect is in the oscillator section, this will not be possible and the horizontal sweep will be considerably off-frequency, but can be locked-in. Figure 8-10 shows how a loss of horizontal synchronism appears on the screen. Usually, the cut-up picture sways and weaves around. When the oscillator is synchronized at a multiple of the correct frequency, several compressed pictures appear side by side.

Adjustment of the horizontal synchronizing section depends on the circuit used. For the Synchroguide circuit an oscilloscope should be used for adjusting the blocking oscillator and the stabilizing coil according to manufacturer's instructions. For the other type of circuit, the hold control is set about half way between either end and the tuned circuit is adjusted to correct synchronization. Switch channels to make sure that the picture locks-in immediately each time.

Defects due to insufficient horizontal sweep are indicated by a narrow, compressed picture. If only one side of the picture is compressed, the RC wave-shaping network may be defective. Most frequently, the sweep signal is weak or has disappeared entirely, so that the high voltage is insufficient to illuminate the screen and nothing at all appears on the picture tube. Check for loss of output amplifier signal by touching the top of that tube with a well-insulated screwdriver. Small arcs should appear if a good signal

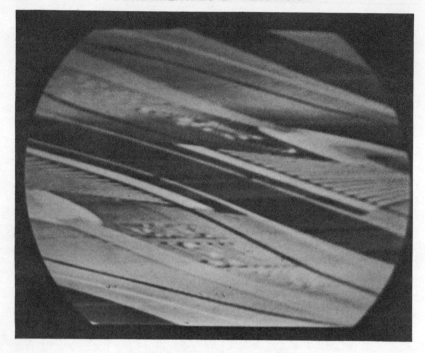

Fig. 8-10. Loss of horizontal sync.

is present. If a strong enough drive signal is applied to the grid of the output amplifier, the grid bias should be at least 40 volts negative. Actually, the horizontal output amplifier tube is usually the culprit and should be exchanged first if no raster appears on the screen. Other defects due to the high voltage section are taken up in the next chapter.

If the deflection yoke itself is defective, and this is quite rare, either a very compressed picture or a single vertical line will appear on the screen. Defects in the damper circuit will cause either a distorted or narrow picture or no raster at all. This type of defect is isolated by eliminating first the output amplifier and oscillator stage as culprits and by measuring the B+ boost voltage. This voltage will also be low or missing completely if the sweep signal is weak or if the output amplifier is defective.

The reader should refer to the manufacturer's data and study the particular circuit whenever horizontal sweep troubles are encountered, because this section is one of the most complex of the entire receiver. The above adjustment and troubleshooting suggestions are only intended as a general guide and cannot take the place of detailed instructions for each type of receiver.

Review Questions

1. What is the principle of automatic frequency control?
2. Which resistor in Figure 8-2 feeds the oscillator signal to the comparator stage?
3. Where, in Figure 8-2, is the error voltage applied to the oscillator?
4. How does the horizontal hold adjustment affect the oscillator frequency?
5. Which LC network in Figure 8-2 serves to stabilize the oscillator?
6. What is the purpose of R3, C3, and C4 in Figure 8-3?
7. Which components in the circuit of Figure 8-3 determine the final sawtooth and pulse voltage waveform?
8. What is the resonant frequency of L1 and C5 in Figure 8-3?
9. What is the function of R4 in Figure 8-3?
10. Why does the transistor oscillator of Figure 8-4 need a buffer stage?
11. How does the horizontal hold control in Figure 8-4 affect the oscillator frequency?
12. What causes the high voltage pulses during the horizontal retrace period?
13. What is the function of R2 in Figure 8-5?
14. Why are the deflection coils in the transistor circuit of Figure 8-6 connected in parallel?
15. Why is a damping diode necessary?
16. What is the function of L1, C3, and C4 in Figure 8-5?
17. What is the effect on the picture when the deflection yoke is not pushed towards the screen?
18. What would appear on the screen if the horizontal oscillator were locked in at 31,500 cps?
19. What symptom indicates an open circuit in the horizontal deflection coils?
20. How can the raster on the screen be tilted?

HIGH VOLTAGE CIRCUITS

We have mentioned earlier in this book that the second anode of the picture tube requires a very high voltage, usually over 12,000 volts. In this chapter we shall deal with the peculiarities inherent in high voltage circuits.

Corona. In basic electricity we learned that the distance across which an arc can jump depends on the voltage and not on the current. We also know that arcing ionizes the air, creates ozone, and produces a peculiar odor. There is another effect, called *corona,* that takes place when the charge on a conductor leaks off into the surrounding air. This happens only at very high voltages and the origin of corona is usually a sharp point, rather than a smooth, large surface. Corona appears as a purplish glow, surrounding the sharp point and fading into the distance. This is quite different from the bluish glow observed in some vacuum tubes due to internal gas ionization. At the same time, a fine hissing sound is heard and the characteristic odor of arcing is noticeable. Corona is not desirable in TV high-voltage supplies because it reduces the available high voltage going to the picture tube, it frequently interferes with other parts of the set, and it usually leads to arcing.

Arcing. Arcing is a very obvious and frequent defect in TV receiver, high-voltage power supplies. It can occur either because dirt has accumulated and forms a lower resistance path between the high voltage and ground or because sharp points shorten the path. Arcing is more likely to occur when the humidity is high. In higher altitudes, where the air is thinner, it is a considerable problem. When arcing occurs, it interferes with the picture as well as sound. Its source can usually be located very simply.

X-rays. High voltage circuits are often thought to present another potential danger, the emission of X-rays. Recent surveys, a number of different investigations, and over 16 years of TV repair and test work have so far failed to show any proof that the high-voltage power supplies used in TV receivers emit dangerous X-rays. Nevertheless, the higher voltages used in color TV can theoretically emit "soft" X-rays and these supplies are therefore shielded a little more. Color tubes themselves usually contain a grounded outer shield. For all practical purposes, the amount of high voltage power used in either color or monochrome receivers could produce only such small doses of X-ray radiation that, considering the distance we normally are from the source, no measureable danger exists.

HIGH VOLTAGE SERVICING PRECAUTIONS

While X-rays are not among the active dangers of high voltage work, a number of precautions should be observed before attempting to service any high voltage circuitry. Since all high-voltage TV sections obtain their voltage by rectifying the 15,750 cps horizontal flyback pulse, a filter capacitor is used at the rectifier output. When the set is turned off, even though the line cord plug may be disconnected, the high voltage capacitor may remain charged for as long as 15 minutes; when the high voltage wire is touched, the investigator may receive a healthy jolt. Also, even though the circuit diagram shows no high voltage capacitor, the capacitance between the second anode coating inside the picture tube and the grounded outer coating serves as a filter and is large enough to store a noticeable charge. For this reason, the high voltage points should always be discharged first with a grounded clip lead or screwdriver before any of them are touched.

When checking the operating set for the presence of high voltage, many experienced technicians will reach in with a well-insulated screwdriver and carefully approach the top caps of the horizontal output amplifier, the high voltage rectifier, and the high voltage connector on the picture tube. This is safe only if the technician is well insulated from the screwdriver and if great care is taken. If the screwdriver is grounded, the resulting arc can damage the high voltage rectifier, but as long as a very high resistance path exists between the screwdriver and ground, only a weak purplish discharge will be seen. This is a sufficient indication of the presence of high voltage.

High voltage sections are carefully designed to provide maximum insulation, avoid sharp points, and reduce the likelihood of arcing due to dust accumulation. They are always located in a separate, screened-off portion of the receiver that can only be opened by removing the a-c power to the receiver. This a-c interlock means that the technician must use a "cheater" cord for servicing. It is absolutely essential that the high voltage section be closed again and the interlock be restored before the technician closes the receiver up. The shock due to the high voltage, even though it is at a low current, is sufficient to cause many injuries in addition to deep and very painful burns.

If any of the high voltage portions must be repaired, be sure to make all solder connections smooth and avoid any sharp points. The use of "corona dope" or insulating varnish increases the insulation and helps reduce the chances for arcing or corona. Usually the socket of the high voltage rectifier contains some protection against corona, such as a smooth brass shell or ring that establishes a high voltage field around the socket and therefore avoids corona discharges from the pins.

FLYBACK TRANSFORMERS

The precautions against arcing and corona are not limited to the rectifier. The transformer that generates the high voltage pulses must also be properly insulated.

Figure 9-1 shows a typical flyback transformer. It is immediately apparent that it differs considerably from the audio and power transformers with which we are familiar. Because it must operate on pulses with a 15,750-cps repetition rate, it must be able to at least pass that frequency. Actually, the flyback pulses contain harmonics that require a transformer frequency response well up into 100 kc. In order not to waste any of this energy, the Q of the transformer must be high. That is the reason why ferrite cores are used and why the entire transformer is well insulated from the chassis.

To avoid the possibility of arcing or corona, the high voltage windings are covered with a special insulating material and the connections for the output amplifier and high voltage rectifier tubes are also covered with insulation or are smooth, spring-wire clips.

The operation of the high voltage section is very simple, as can be seen from the circuit diagram of Figure 9-2. We know from the

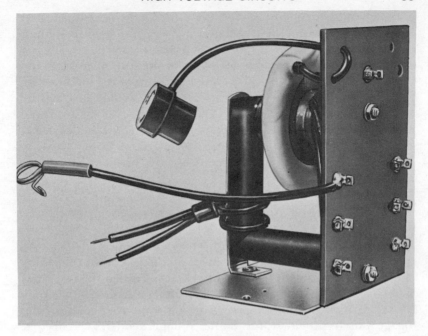

Fig. 9-1. A typical flyback transformer. (Stancor)

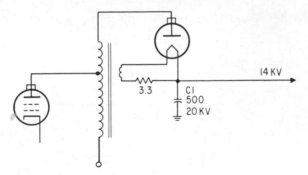

Fig. 9-2. A typical high voltage circuit.

preceding chapter that high voltage pulses appear at the plate of the output amplifier. By means of a high Q autotransformer winding, these pulses are further stepped up and connected to the plate of the rectifier. This plate connection is always a top cap. The cathode of the rectifier tube provides the rectified pulses, which are filtered by capacitor C1. In some late model receivers, a 2-watt series resistor goes between the cathode and the capacitor consisting of the inner and outer coating of the picture tube.

To light the filaments of the rectifier tube, a loop of well-insulated wire is passed around the transformer core. This picks up enough r-f energy for the 1.5-volt filaments. A small resistor, usually 3.3 ohms, is connected in series with this filament loop to limit the current to a safe value. Because the solder joints of the high voltage connections in the filament and cathode circuit could cause arcing or corona, they are all contained in the tube socket assembly where they are either covered by insulation or protected by a corona shield.

These high voltage rectifier tubes use the filament directly as cathode.

COLOR TV HIGH VOLTAGE SECTIONS

In color TV receivers, the high voltage section is basically the same as that in monochrome receivers and is also part of the horizontal flyback section. The only differences between the two types of receiver are that a higher voltage, usually about 25,000 volts (25 kv), is used in the color receiver and some regulation of the voltage must be provided and another voltage, about 6 kv, is needed for focusing. As seen in Figure 9-3, this focus voltage is obtained from a separate rectifier that operates like the others. A resistive voltage divider is sometimes used to adjust the focus voltage.

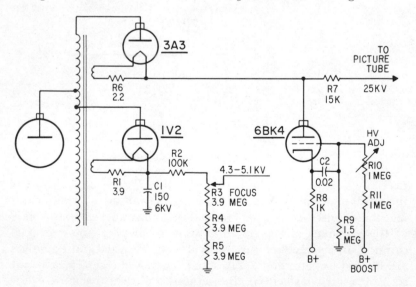

Fig. 9-3. The high voltage section of a color receiver.

To regulate the high voltage for the second anode, a special regulator tube, also using a plate top cap, has been developed. This tube is used in a circuit that causes the plate current to increase as the plate voltage increases, thereby keeping the voltage to the picture tube steady. Why this type of regulation is necessary will be explained in detail in the chapter devoted to color picture tube circuitry (Chapter 15). Adjustment of the grid bias on the regulator sets the actual level of voltage at which regulation occurs. To avoid cathode-heater breakdown, the 6.3-volt filaments of this tube are connected to a special "floating" winding on the power transformer similar to those of some damper tubes.

ADJUSTMENT AND TROUBLESHOOTING

In black-and-white receivers, the high voltage cannot be adjusted without also adjusting the horizontal sweep. (As we have just seen, in color TV sets there is an adjustment in the grid of the high voltage regulator tube.) To diagnose high voltage troubles one need only keep in mind that arcing and corona can occur at any high voltage point. These are really simple mechanical defects that can be located by inspection. A reduction of high voltage can be suspected whenever the lines of the picture cannot be focused sharply or a bright picture cannot be obtained. It is possible to confuse these symptoms with natural aging of the picture tube or even with a weak or gassy picture tube. To make sure that the high voltage operates correctly, the voltage must be measured. Special high voltage probes are available that convert any vtvm into a high voltage meter. Always check the high voltage with the picture-tube second anode lead disconnected, because a gassy picture tube can draw excessive current, giving the impression of insufficient high voltage.

When the high voltage is missing entirely, the defect may be in the horizontal output amplifier or even in the oscillator. Check all voltages on the output amplifier, except the plate voltage, and then measure the B+ boost voltage. If there is no light in the high voltage rectifier, this tube may have an open filament. Occasionally the high voltage capacitor or the flyback transformer becomes defective, a defect that can be checked by ohmmeter measurement. Many older receivers contain a fuse in series with the B+ or the B+ voltage boost that is soldered onto terminals on the flyback transformer. If that fuse is open, there will be no high voltage.

If a defective flyback transformer must be replaced, be sure to use the exact replacement part. It is then usually necessary to adjust the horizontal output section and all circuits obtaining signals from it.

REVIEW QUESTIONS

1. Why is corona undesirable in TV receivers?
2. Where will corona appear?
3. How can corona be cured?
4. What precautions are necessary before the high voltage section can be serviced?
5. Why are flyback transformer cores insulated from ground?
6. How is the filament power for the h-v rectifier obtained?
7. Why are the filaments of the h-v regulator tube in Figure 9-3 connected to a special winding on the power transformer?
8. What is the purpose of the 3.3-ohm resistor in Figure 9-2?
9. What is the polarity of the flyback pulses at the plate of the h-v rectifier?
10. What happens to the h-v if the horizontal oscillator tube is removed?

THE SYNC SEPARATOR SECTION

We know from Chapter 2 that at the start of each line of the picture a horizontal sync pulse is transmitted and that a vertical pulse is sent out at the beginning of each field. In Chapters 7 and 8 we have seen how these sync pulses are used to synchronize the vertical and horizontal sweep sections, respectively. In this chapter we shall show how the sync pulses themselves are separated from the composite picture signal.

Referring back to Chapter 2 and Figures 2-6, 2-7, and 2-8, we remember that the sync pulses ride atop the blanking pulses and are always well into the "blacker-than-black" region. Sync separation consists of two distinct steps: first the sync pulses are removed from the composite video signal and then they are separated according to their frequency. In practically all TV receivers these two steps are performed in two adjoining stages, generally called the *sync separator section*.

SYNC CLIPPING

To remove the sync pulses from the composite video is rather simple because their amplitude is greater than that of the video. A grid leak bias circuit is usually used to clip off the positive pulses. This is illustrated in the first half of the double triode of Figure 10-1, where C1 and R1 form a grid leak bias network that charges up during the sync pulse portion so that the tube is completely cut-off during the video portion. This permits only the positive sync pulse to be amplified. The plate voltage of this stage is kept low to accomplish limiting of the amplified sync pulses. Limiting is necessary to prevent any noise pulses that might be riding on the

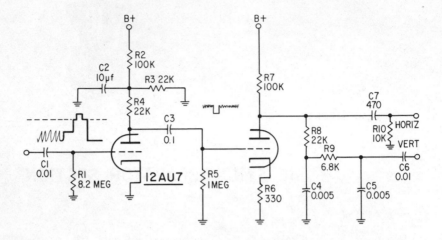

Fig. 10-1. A typical sync separator section.

sync pulse from coming through and possibly triggering the sweep sections erroneously. The second triode stage of Figure 10-1 serves as a simple inverting amplifier to provide sync pulses of sufficient amplitude and of the desired positive polarity.

INTEGRATING AND DIFFERENTIATING

The second step, the separation of the two frequencies, is accomplished with RC networks. The vertical sync pulse occurs at a 60-cps rate and, although we have seen in Chapter 2 that it contains horizontal equalizing pulses, only the 60-cps component is important as vertical sync information. On the other hand, the horizontal sync pulse has a repetition rate of 15,750 cps and the 60-cps component due to the vertical sync period must be removed for the horizontal sweep synchronizing action. These two signals can be separated by high and low pass filters. The high pass filter will permit only the horizontal sync pulses to pass and the low pass filter will allow only the 60-cps component through. In actual practice the networks used can be considered as such filters, but because we deal here with pulses the terms *integration* and *differentiation* are used.

Figure 10-2 shows the basic networks for integration and differentiation, as well as their response to a pulse. We see from it that the integrating network is really a low pass filter that removes

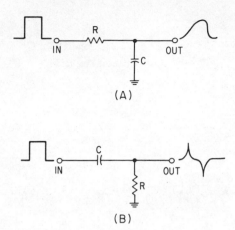

Fig. 10-2. RC networks: (A) integrating network; (B) differentiating network.

the high frequency components. The differentiating network does the opposite and lets only the high frequency components through.

Now we can understand the remainder of the circuit of Figure 10-1, which shows the differentiating network consisting of C7 and R10 as the output for the horizontal sync pulse. The vertical sync pulse requires several stages of integration because it contains the equalizing pulses; the network consisting of R8, R9, C4, and C5 meets that requirement.

Figure 10-3 shows the relationship between the original vertical sync pulse period, the output of the integrating network, the output of the differentiating network, and the horizontal and vertical sweep signals. The "painting" and retrace time relations are slightly distorted to give a clearer picture of the action of the integrating and differentiating networks.

TRANSISTOR SYNC SEPARATOR

In transistor receivers the sync separation section performs the identical function that it performs in vacuum-tube receivers and therefore also contains the equivalent of two triode stages. Figure 10-4 shows such a circuit. Note that the first transistor contains base bias equivalent to grid leak bias due to the RC network R2–C2, and that the collector voltage is also limited to a value less than the full

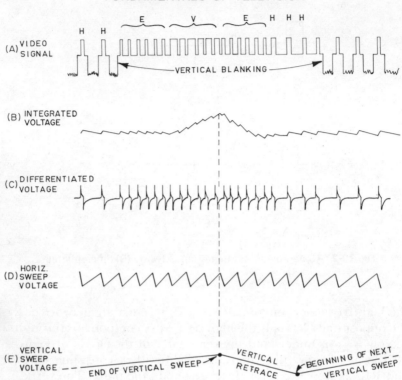

Fig. 10-3. Vertical sync pulse integration and differentiation.

B+. The second stage is an inverting amplifier that drives the differentiating and integrating networks. Because of the relatively low output impedance of the transistor, the values are different than those used in tube circuits, but the same principles apply. The vertical integrator consists of only one stage, but the series diode and the method of injecting the vertical sync pulses in a third winding of the blocking oscillator transformer help the low pass filter action. This transistor circuit makes use of the different polarity requirements of the n-p-n and p-n-p transistors to minimize power supply problems.

NOISE SUPPRESSION

One of the problems in synchronization, especially of the horizontal sweep, is the action of strong noise pulses that can ride in during the video signal. They can cause a false triggering of the horizontal sweep and therefore give the appearance of tearing of

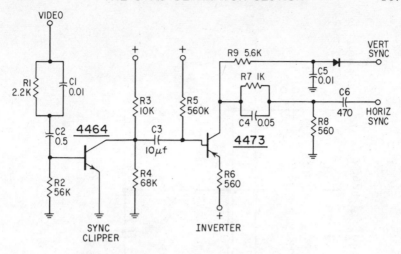

Fig. 10-4. A transistor sync separator circuit.

the picture. In the vertical section this problem is not so severe because the duration of the vertical sync pulse is much longer than most noise bursts and the integrating circuit will tend to remove all sharp, random spikes from the vertical sync.

When the noise pulse amplitude reaches into the "blacker-than-black" region, the clipping action of the sync pulse clipper will clip it, just like a sync pulse. If the noise is strong enough, noise pulses might even add up to raise the grid leak bias beyond the sync pulse level and prevent the separation of the sync pulses from the video signal. The presence of such strong noise pulses will be apparent in the picture in the form of black streaks as well as the tearing of horizontal lines due to loss of horizontal synchronization. Many recent receivers use a specially-developed dual pentode to perform the separation of synchronizing pulses and, at the same time, provide gated automatic gain control. (This latter action is described in more detail in Chapter. 20, which covers special TV circuits.)

The sync pulse separator circuit of Figure 10-5 consists of the right half of the two pentode sections, which have all elements except the suppressor grid and the plate in common. This pentode acts like a grid leak clipper and plate limiter with one other vital feature: video signals, and with them the sync pulses, are applied both at the control and suppressor grids. Those applied to the control grid come from the video detector and those on the suppressor grid come from the video amplifier and are of opposite polarity

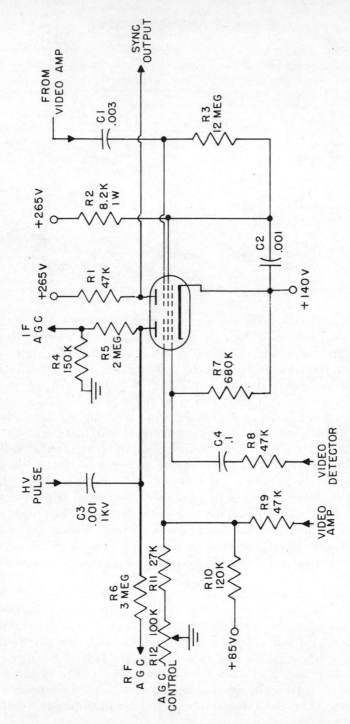

Fig. 10-5. Noise gate sync separator and agc.

and greater amplitude. The effect of this is that the suppressor grid allows no signals to pass unless a large amplitude pulse from the video amplifier is present; i.e., nothing at all can appear at the plate of that tube except during the sync pulse period. Only at that time are the sync pulses from the video detector amplified and clipped. The main advantage of this circuit is that it keeps all the noise and interference that might ride through on the video signal from reaching the sync separator output. The sync pulse output is passed through separate filters, as described in the preceding paragraphs, and is then applied to control the vertical and horizontal sweep sections.

COLOR BURST SEPARATION

In color TV receivers, the horizontal and vertical sync pulses are separated just as they are in monochrome sets, but an additional sync signal must be removed from the composite video signal. This is the 8-cycle, 3.58-mc color reference burst that is transmitted during the blanking portion of each horizontal sweep, as explained in Chapter 5 and illustrated in Figure 5-9. To remove this 8-cycle burst, the composite video signal is applied to the color burst separator stage, a typical circuit of which is shown in Figure 10-6.

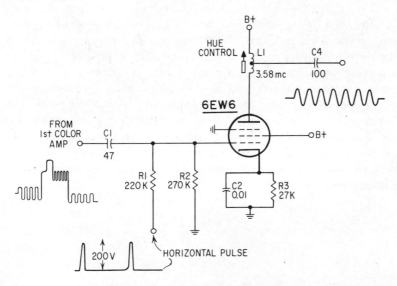

Fig. 10-6. The color burst separator circuit.

Due to the cathode self-bias, this pentode is normally cut-off and no signal reaches the plate. Only when the horizontal flyback pulse is applied to the grid through R1 is the negative bias overcome sufficiently to allow the sync pulse portion of the composite video signal to be amplified. The grid coupling capacitor C1 is small and favors the 3.58-mc burst over the 15,750-cps fundamental of the blanking portion. At the plate the hue control coil L1 is tuned to resonate at 3.58 mc with the circuit and plate capacity, providing maximum gain of the color sync burst. From there the burst is supplied to the color sync section where it controls the color reference oscillator, as will be described in detail in Chapter 17.

The adjustment of the hue control coil not only tunes the plate circuit, but, because the color burst is taken off at a tap, it also affects the phase of the color burst and the hue of the resultant picture.

ADJUSTMENT AND TROUBLESHOOTING

As we have seen, there are no adjustments in most of the sync separator circuits. In servicing TV receivers we can usually assume that the sync separator section operates correctly if either vertical or horizontal sync pulses appear to be present. Most defects that can occur in this section can be located simply by signal tracing or often just by logical considerations. If the horizontal sync pulses seem to perform properly, but the vertical hold cannot be adjusted, the defect is either in the vertical oscillator or, possibly, in the integrating network. In many sets these networks are a single, packaged item, which is difficult to troubleshoot stage by stage. The entire network should then be replaced. If neither vertical or horizontal sync action is possible, then the defect invariably is in the sync separator. Aside from obvious tube defects, any of the operating components can become defective and cause loss of all sync pulses. The defective part can be located by voltage and resistance measurements.

Review Questions

1. What two functions are performed in the grid and plate of the first stage of the circuit in Figure 10-1?

2. What type of circuit is used to remove the horizontal sync pulses from the vertical sync?

3. What type of circuit is used to separate the vertical sync components and let only the horizontal sync through?

4. Name the components that provide the differentiating action in the circuit of Figure 10-4.

5. How does strong noise interference appear in the picture?

6. What is the function of the signal from the video amplifier in the circuit of Figure 10-5?

7. Which components in Figure 10-5 determine the sync clipping action?

8. What cuts off the tube in Figure 10-6 during the video signal?

9. Why is only the color sync burst amplified in Figure 10-6?

10. Which network is most likely to be defective if the picture rolls up or down?

THE VIDEO SECTION

The video signal that represents the television picture must have a much wider range than the sound frequencies audible to the human ear. We can generally only hear frequencies up to about 15,000 cycles, but we can see a tremendous amount of fine detail. Television signal standards, as explained in Chapter 2, provide for a video signal bandwidth of up to 4 mc; a limitation based on the maximum fine detail, or resolution, possible with a 525 line picture. (French television stations offer an 800 line picture which shows much more fine detail and also requires a much greater video signal bandwidth.)

VIDEO SIGNAL CHARACTERISTICS

The video signal contains elements of all frequencies up to 4 mc. The frequency response curve of the video sections should therefore be relatively flat up to 4 mc, as illustrated in Figure 11-1. Ideally, the response should be that indicated by the straight dotted line, but it is the solid line response that is more likely to be actually realized. At 4.5 mc there must be a sharp dip in the response curve because the audio signal is 4.5 mc above the carrier of the video signal and this 4.5-mc beat signal would show up as interference in the TV picture. Neither vacuum tubes nor transistors have a flat frequency response up to 4 mc, mostly because of the inherent plate or collector capacity, which shunts the output impedance and, at the higher frequencies, lowers the effective impedance. Later in this chapter various methods for obtaining the desired frequency response will be explained.

112

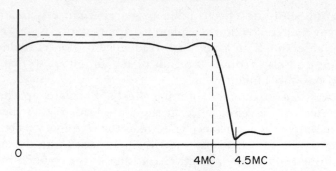

Fig. 11-1. Video frequency response.

In color TV receivers, several video signals are used. The brightness or Y signal corresponds to the black-and-white signal and therefore has the same video section. All color information is contained on the color subcarrier at 3.58 mc and this signal must be amplified separately before the color elements are demodulated. The frequency response of the bandpass amplifier section that handles the 3.58-mc subcarrier is shown in Figure 11-2; it includes sufficient bandwidth to pass all color elements. Unlike the brightness amplifier, the bandpass amplifier should not amplify all signals from dc on up, but only the desired frequency range. To accomplish this, the amplifier uses broadly-tuned resonant circuits, considered in more detail later in this chapter.

HIGH FREQUENCY PEAKING

The normal frequency response of a particular amplifier depends largely on the plate load and the internal plate capacity. To get a broader frequency response, the plate load can be made lower

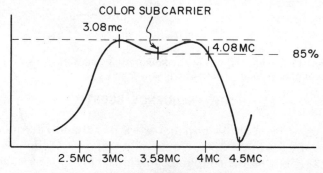

Fig. 11-2. Color bandpass response.

so that the shunting effect of the plate capacitance is relatively small. No matter how low the plate load impedance is, however, there is a definite limit to the high frequency response. Reducing the plate load also reduces the gain of the amplifier, so that this method has only limited value.

One way to overcome the shunting effect of the plate capacitance is to insert a series inductance in the plate load so that the impedance due to the inductance goes up as the frequency increases. Another way is to use a small inductance in series with the signal take-off point so that the inductive reactance of the coil neutralizes the capacitive reactance of the plate capacity. In most television video sections both types of peaking coils are used, as illustrated in the circuit of Figure 11-3A. The series coil L1 is shown here shunted by R1, which helps to broaden the peak in the response curve. A sharp peak could cause damped oscillations which appear as multiple lines, or ringing, whenever a sharp transition from white to black occurs in the picture.

The same high frequency problem exists in the video detector and at the input to the video amplifier. Again, series and shunt peaking coils are used to extend the response of the overall video section to approximately 4 mc.

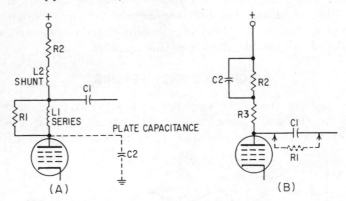

Fig. 11-3. Video frequency compensating networks: (A) high frequency peaking; (B) low frequency boost.

LOW FREQUENCY BOOST

We know from audio amplifier work that the low frequency response of a vacuum tube or transistor amplifier is limited not by that stage, but by the coupling capacitor. This capacitor increases in impedance as the frequency goes down, which produces the attenuating effect of a series resistor between stages. To overcome the reduction in signal between stages, the coupling capacitor can be made large or, at best, coupling can be direct, without any capacitor. In fact, some TV receivers use direct coupling between the video detector and the video amplifier and from there to the picture tube. In these circuits, the low frequency response is automatically perfect and no compensation is necessary.

In many sets, however, d-c connection is not used because of power-supply voltage problems and some compensation at the lower video signals is necessary. Figure 11-3B shows a common scheme for boosting the low frequency response. Similar to the shunt peaking coil for the high frequency case, another plate load is inserted here which is most effective at lower frequencies. R2 and C2 form the low frequency boost network. At higher frequencies, C2 is a low impedance and the effective plate load is R3 in series with R2-C2. For frequencies below a few hundred cycles, C2 becomes a high enough impedance to increase substantially the total plate load. R1, shown in dotted lines, represents the series impedance due to the coupling capacitor C1 at the lower frequencies.

If the low frequency response of the video section is poor, this is usually apparent by smearing and uneven shading of larger dark areas.

A TYPICAL VIDEO AMPLIFIER

Although actual video amplifier circuits vary between different manufacturers and receiver models, the circuit shown in Figure 11-4 is representative of many late model TV sets. Starting at the

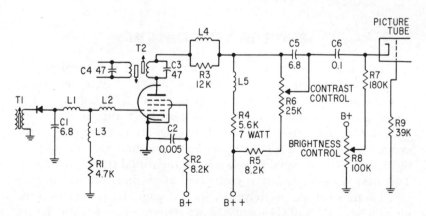

Fig. 11-4. A typical video amplifier circuit.

video detector, we can see the use of various peaking coils. The LC network consisting of C1 and L1, L2, and L3 serves a double purpose. It acts as a filter to remove the i-f signal and also compensates for the grid capacity of the video amplifier to maintain a good response curve up to 4.5 mc.

In the plate circuit, the 4.5-mc sound signal is removed by the sharply-tuned transformer, T2, and its resonant circuits. The high frequency peaking coils, L4 and L5, are connected as series and shunt networks, respectively. The plate load resistance of R4 is shunted by the contrast control and its series limiting resistor, R5. C5 merely compensates for the high frequency reduction when the contrast control is set for low video signal amplitudes.

The d-c bias between grid and cathode of the picture tube is determined by the brightness control, R8. C6, the coupling capacitor from the video detector to the picture tube, could limit the low frequency response, but its relatively large value and the fact that it connects between two low impedance points maintain sufficient low frequency response in this circuit to avoid the need for a special boosting network. In some earlier TV receivers, complete d-c coupling is maintained from the detector to the picture tube, while in others, coupling capacitors are used freely. To get an idea of the impedances in the video output circuit of Figure 11-4, remember that R4, the effective load, is 5.6K, shunted by approximately 33K. This source impedance of approximately 5000 ohms drives C6, which looks like a 15,000 ohm impedance at 100 cps, into at least 180,000 ohms, R7. The attenuation due to C6, even at 100 cps, is therefore not very severe.

TRANSISTOR VIDEO AMPLIFIERS

A typical transistor video amplifier circuit is shown in Figure 11-5. Two stages of video amplification are used here because of the difficulty of obtaining a large enough voltage swing in a single stage. The video detector circuit is essentially the same as that used in the tube version and its output signals are generally in the order of a few volts. At the collector of the first video amplifier, the 4.5-mc sound signal is removed by the tuned transformer, T2. This first video amplifier is connected as emitter follower to provide enough current to drive the second stage. L2 is a series peaking coil, and L3 and C4 form a series resonant trap for the 4.5-mc sound signal to keep it out of the second video stage.

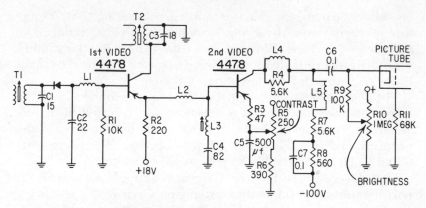

Fig. 11-5. A transistor video amplifier.

The second video amplifier circuit is similar to that of a tube version in that it contains both series and shunt peaking and also has a low frequency boost network. R8, a 560-ohm series resistor, is shunted by C7, which presents about 15,000-ohms impedance at 100 cps. At the low frequencies, R8 effectively increases the collector impedance by about 10% and therefore boosts the signal accordingly. The contrast control here is simply a d-c bias setting in the emitter circuit. Note that the emitter of the second stage is returned to ground while the collector is connected to −100 volts. The picture tube connections are practically the same as in the tube version.

While the circuit of Figure 11-5 is typical of transistor video amplifiers, other arrangements will be found as manufacturer's designs vary and as new transistor types become available. The principles of high and low frequency compensation, however, apply to all transistor circuits as well as to tube amplifiers.

VIDEO SIGNAL POLARITY

We know from Chapter 2 that video signals must appear at the picture tube in such a way that during the blanking period the electron beam is cut-off. Understanding this calls for a definition of black and white polarity. In the typical circuits of Figures 11-4 and 11-5, the video signal has been applied to the cathode of the picture tube, which means that the blanking pulses must drive the cathode positive, beyond the cut-off bias of the electron gun. If the brightness control is set so that the screen is just about dark when no video signal appears, then signals corresponding to white picture portions must drive the cathode negative to reduce the cathode-grid bias and allow more electrons to flow. Blanking pulses must drive the cathode more positive to create the "blacker-than-black" condition during the return of the electron beam.

The polarity of the video signal depends on the connection of the video detector diode. If this connection were reversed in the examples, the polarity of the video signal would be reversed and the picture would look like a photographic negative. The white areas would be black and the black areas would be white.

In receivers where the video signal is applied to the grid, its polarity must be such that the blanking pulses drive the grid negative with respect to the cathode. Figure 11-6 illustrates the principles of polarity for both types of picture tube connections. It occasionally happens that a defective video amplifier stage causes

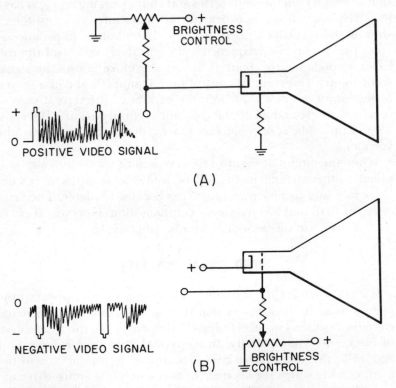

Fig. 11-6. Video signal polarity: (A) cathode connection; (B) grid connection.

the picture to appear as a photographic negative. The usual remedy is replacement of the video amplifier tube. Polarity of the video signal is an important thing to remember when a defective video detector is replaced. Be sure always to check the polarity of the diode before soldering it into place.

D-C RESTORATION

The composite video signal contains all blanking pulses lined up at the same level. All white levels and the various shades of grey line up at the same respective levels as well. This effectively means that the picture signal contains a d-c element in addition to the a-c portions. When this signal is passed through coupling capacitors, the d-c element is blocked and lost. In the video amplifier circuits of Figures 11-4 and 11-5, however, direct connections are used from the video detector to the plate of the output stage and, therefore, at least that far, the d-c component is retained. Only at the final coupling capacitor is the d-c level eliminated from the picture tube. In many earlier TV receivers, one of two schemes was used to maintain this d-c level. Either the output stage was coupled directly to the picture tube grid or cathode and a grid leak circuit restored the d-c element at the video amplifier, or else a diode restored the d-c level at the picture tube. In more recent receivers, the picture tube design itself permits grid leak action to take place so that the d-c level is effectively restored.

In the examples shown, the coupling capacitor and the cathode series resistors have a combined time constant which permits the capacitor to charge up during the blanking period so that it will maintain a fairly constant d-c potential across the cathode resistor during the "painting" period. If this d-c level is completely lost, the picture will have uneven background shading when the scene shows large areas of white or light grey. The effect of the d-c level loss on the sync sections is more serious, but since these modern receivers use direct coupling from the video detector to the sync pulse take-off point, this is no problem here.

ADJUSTMENT AND TROUBLESHOOTING

Aside from the contrast and brightness controls, which are accessible to the set owner, there is only one service adjustment that affects the video amplifier. This is the 4.5-mc trap, or sound coupling circuit, which should be tuned for maximum 4.5-mc response, preferably with a 4.5-mc signal from a generator, although the transmitted sound signal can also be used.

Troubleshooting the video section is always indicated by the loss or distortion of the video signal, usually combined with loss of the horizontal and vertical sync pulses. If a raster appears on the screen, but no video signal can be produced, the video amplifier is the prime suspect. Loss of fine detail points to a defective peaking coil or to a misalignment or defect in the i-f stages. Peaking coils can be checked with the ohmmeter. Smearing of dark lines into adjoining white picture portions points to loss of low frequency response. If a reverse, or negative picture appears, the defect may be either in the detector or the video amplifier itself. All defects occurring before the sync pulse take-off point will also appear as loss or at least unstable horizontal synchronization.

Review Questions

1. What factors determine the high frequency response of a vacuum-tube amplifier?
2. How does a shunt peaking coil increase the high frequency response?
3. What component in an RC amplifier usually limits the low frequency response?
4. Which component in the circuit of Figure 11-3B provides low frequency boost?
5. How does poor, low frequency response appear in the picture?
6. Which coil in the plate circuit of Figure 11-4 provides series peaking?
7. Which component in the circuit of Figure 11-5 provides low frequency boost?
8. If the video signal goes to the picture-tube cathode, what must be the blanking pulse polarity?
9. How is loss of the d-c level apparent in the picture?
10. What causes a "negative" type of picture to appear on the screen?

THE I-F AMPLIFIER AND DETECTOR

From Chapter 6 we know that television receivers, like all super-heterodyne receivers, have a section that amplifies the received signals at the intermediate frequency. In TV, the i-f section is always more complex than in broadcast receivers because it must amplify a wider band of frequencies. Nominally, the picture frequencies range up to 4 mc and the sound i-f is obtained at 4.5 mc, so that it would seem necessary that the i-f amplifier have at least a 4.5-mc wide passband. In actual practice, however, the desired response curve of a good monochrome TV i-f section looks more like the ideal shown in Figure 12-1.

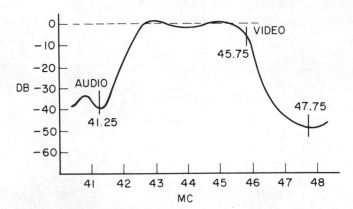

Fig. 12-1. Monochrome i-f response.

The response curve dips sharply at either end because of the beat signals that could be obtained from adjacent channels. Note that the nominal video carrier of 45.75 mc is located on a slope.

121

This point corresponds to the low frequency portion of the video signal while the 42-mc point corresponds to the high video frequencies. A dip at 41.25 mc is intended to keep the sound signal level low enough so that it does not interfere in the picture, while the 47.75-mc dip prevents the sound of an adjacent channel from appearing in the picture.

While practically all new TV sets use the 41- to 45-mc i-f, there are still quite a few old models in use that use the 21- to 25-mc i-f. All of the response requirements are essentially the same, but a 4-mc bandwidth is easier to obtain at 40 mc than at 20 mc. For this and a number of other reasons connected with interference from other communication services, all manufacturers now use the 40-mc i-f band.

The color receiver's i-f response curve is shown in Figure 12-2. Because of the addition of the color subcarrier and its sidebands, it is essential that the flat portion of the response extend to at least 41.75 mc, which means that the attenuation at the sound i-f of 41.25 mc must be much sharper. To avoid any chance of getting sound into the color signal, the sound i-f carrier must be about 60 db down. This is a much stricter requirement than the 40 db attenuation on the monochrome response curve of Figure 12-1. The flatness of the color set's i-f response curve is usually much better than in monochrome sets. We shall see shortly how frequency response curves such as those in Figures 12-1 and 12-2 are obtained in actual circuitry and shall then understand why the i-f sections in color sets are invariably so complex.

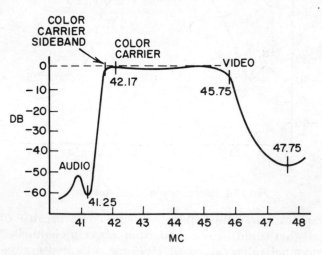

Fig. 12-2. Color i-f response.

Fig. 12-3. Single stage response with loading.

PRINCIPLES OF STAGGER TUNING

The reader will know from broadcast radio what response curve to expect from a single stage of amplification with a single-tuned circuit. A reminder of the appearance of such a response curve and the effect of resistive loading appears in Figure 12-3. The loading is increased as the shunting resistance gets lower, and the response flattens out, but the gain at maximum is reduced.

If two stages tuned to different frequencies are connected in cascade (stagger tuning), their individual response curves effectively add up as illustrated by the solid curve of Figure 12-4A by simply adding amplitude on the scope screen at each frequency. If one of the stages has a tuned attenuation network, its effect will be the negative of the addition; it will subtract at each frequency, as illustrated in Figure 12-4B. Both addition and subtraction are used in i-f amplifier sections to produce the special response curves required. At least five response curves are usually added, as illustrated in Figure 12-5, and at least two subtractions take place; they have been omitted in Figure 12-5, but their effect is apparent in the steep slope at 41.25 mc and the drop-off at 47.75 mc.

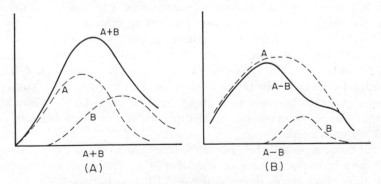

Fig. 12-4. (A) Adding response curves. (B) Subtracting response curves.

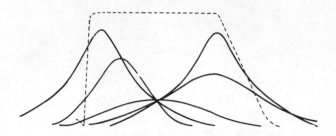

Fig. 12-5. Adding five response curves.

I-F TRAPS

Cathode Trap. We have spoken of subtraction or *tuned attenuation* in i-f amplifiers; to accomplish this, three types of circuits can be used. The simplest is the *cathode trap*. A parallel resonant circuit (Figure 12-6A) used as cathode load will reduce the gain of the stage at the resonant frequency by developing maximum voltage across the cathode network, leaving very little signal to appear at the plate. This action may be referred to in terms of cathode degeneration at the resonant frequency.

Series Trap. A second type of trap can be located anywhere along the signal path, usually in the grid or plate circuit of a stage, and will act as a near short circuit for the trap frequency. Such a trap is simply a series resonant network. We should remember that a parallel-tuned network has maximum impedance and a series-tuned network has minimum impedance at the resonant frequency. The series-type trap is illustrated in Figure 12-6B.

Absorption Trap. The third type of trap does not even appear to be in the circuit, according to the schematic diagram of Figure 12-6C. It is called an *absorption trap* because it is usually mounted on the same form as some other resonant circuit from which it "absorbs," by electromagnetic coupling, the frequency to which it is tuned. In some sets, the trap is returned to ground, while in many older sets, the LC network is completely unconnected. The trapped energy is dissipated in the resonant circuit itself. Absorption-type traps are always high Q circuits, just like the resonant circuits of wave meters or grid dip oscillators, which operate on the same principle.

All three types of i-f traps will be found in modern TV receivers. Their alignment is part of the overall i-f response adjustment, which is taken up in detail at the end of this chapter.

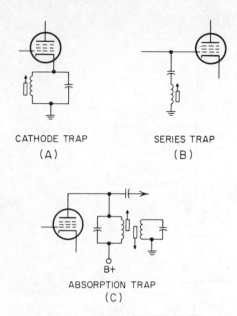

CATHODE TRAP
(A)

SERIES TRAP
(B)

ABSORPTION TRAP
(C)

Fig. 12-6. I-F traps: (A) cathode trap; (B) series trap; (C) absorption trap.

TYPICAL I-F CIRCUITS

A typical i-f amplifier section with its complete circuit is shown in Figure 12-7. The five resonant circuits shown form the response curve and two series traps, L1-C1 and L2-C2, are located at the first i-f amplifier input. Each of the three tubes is a pentode with conventional amplifier connections. The first two stages have their control grids returned to the agc bus, which is a negative bias derived from the video signal. *Automatic gain control* (agc) operates similar to the avc used on broadcast and communications receivers. Where agc is used, the cathode contains a small, unbypassed resistor that serves to stabilize the circuit at low values of grid bias. The third stage is not agc operated and its cathode bias arrangement is bypassed.

Note that each of the tuned circuits is aligned for a different frequency. Because the gain of the first two stages varies with the signal level, these stages are tuned to both sides of the response curve. This means that the entire flat portion changes level as the agc bias changes. If the first two stages were both tuned to one side of the response curve, the agc action would seriously affect the shape of the curve. In many modern TV receivers, some of the

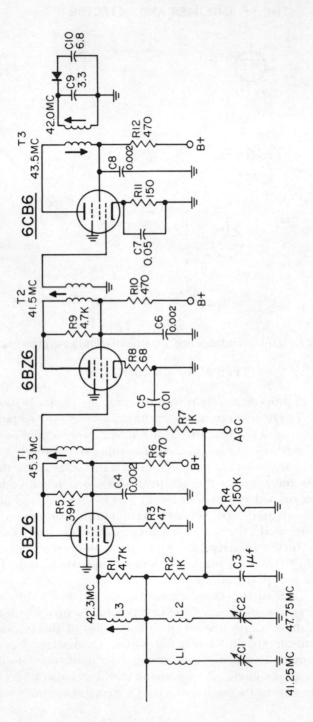

Fig. 12-7. A typical i-f amplifier circuit.

tuned circuits, such as T1 and T2 in Figure 12-7, are bifilar wound transformers (i.e., the primary and secondary windings are intertwined). This provides a single tuning adjustment and a single frequency as compared to T3, which has two separate windings, each tuned to a different frequency.

The video detector follows the last i-f amplifier and is either a semiconductor diode, as in Figure 12-7, or a vacuum-tube diode. Either detector type operates as a conventional rectifier, detecting the amplitude of the i-f modulation envelope. At the output side of the detector there is always some filtering to remove the i-f component and then some video peaking circuits. The video detector also produces a beat signal between the sound and video i-f carrier. This beat signal between the two i-f carriers has a 4.5-mc component that is frequency modulated with the sound signal. Under the so-called intercarrier principle this 4.5-mc beat is used as second i-f for the sound signal. (A detailed description of the intercarrier sound system is found in Chapter 18, which covers all TV sound circuits.)

TRANSISTOR I-F CIRCUITS

In transistor TV receivers, the i-f section does the same job that it performs in tube receivers and uses analogous circuits. Figure 12-8 shows a typical example of an i-f section using p-n-p transistors and a germanium diode video detector. Starting at the left of the figure we find a series-tuned circuit bringing the signal to the base of the first stage with three series traps generating the necessary dips in the response curve. The first and second stages are controlled by the agc bias and all emitters are returned to the positive B+ source. The collector-tuned circuits for the first two stages are series-parallel, single-tuned coils with a small feedback winding and capacitor to neutralize the collector-base capacity. Later model transistors need less of the neutralization because they have less collector-base capacity. This neutralization is similar to that used in high frequency triode amplifiers found in communications receivers.

Another series trap is used in the input to the third i-f stage to reduce the sound i-f and the third stage transformer is double-tuned, as it is in the vacuum-tube version in Figure 12-7.

Note that the video detector of Figure 12-8 contains a pi-filter to reject the i-f component and extend the video frequency response. Because it couples directly to the base of the first video

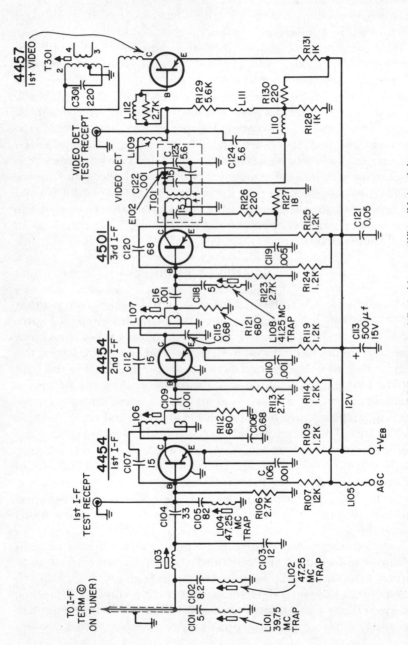

Fig. 12-8. A transistor i-f detector and first video amplifier. (Motorola)

amplifier stage, the d-c return of the detector goes to a slightly positive point, so that some forward bias is always maintained on the video amplifier.

Different transistor i-f circuits may use a different number of tuned circuits and the actual configuration of individual stages may vary, but the essential features of all transistor and vacuum-tube i-f circuits are the same. For this reason, their alignment and troubleshooting is also basically the same. Once the two basic methods of alignment are understood, any i-f circuit can be tackled.

ALIGNMENT AND TROUBLESHOOTING

Before discussing detailed alignment procedures, the most likely defects to be found in i-f stages should be understood. Since the function of the i-f section is to amplify signals over a certain frequency range, the most frequent defect will be loss of amplification. Simple tube substitution will locate the defective stage in 90% of the defects. Occasionally, a component becomes defective and that can be found by signal tracing. If we connect a signal generator at the input to the last stage and still get a signal, that stage is functioning properly. Going forward stage by stage, we will reach a point where the signal is lost; that is the defective stage.

Defects that do not result in total loss of video signals or in very weak signals usually are apparent as loss of either high or low frequencies or beat interference due to defects in the trap circuits. In troubleshooting i-f amplifiers, the circuit diagram and alignment information should always be at hand. It is important to know what the top or bottom tuning adjustment on a transformer can is supposed to tune and which traps are set for which frequencies. Another important factor to remember is that the mixer stage, located in the r-f tuner, is part of the i-f section because its output is tuned by the coupling circuit going to the first i-f stage. I-F alignment may not generally be needed when a tube is replaced, but if any of the other components, particularly the resonant circuits, coils, or capacitors, are defective, a complete alignment will be essential. Poor alignment can cause poor picture detail, smearing of the black portions, sound interference in the picture, poor vertical and horizontal hold, a weak and washed-out picture, and a number of less obvious defects such as hum in the sound and adjacent channel interference. In color sets, the alignment is much more critical and a number of color defects can be traced directly to poor i-f alignment.

Alignment with Signal Generator and VTVM

I-F alignment can be accomplished by either of two methods. The simpler method uses a sweep generator and an oscilloscope that displays the actual frequency response curve while alignment is performed. The second method is more tedious, but requires only a simple signal generator and a vtvm. As illustrated in Figure 12-9, the vtvm is connected to the output of the video detector and the signal generator is tuned to the frequency of the last i-f stage. If a double-tuned transformer is used, as in the previously described typical circuits, first one winding and then the other is aligned, each at the generator frequency called for in the manufacturer's data.

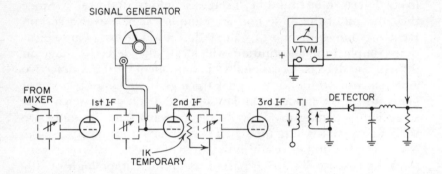

Fig. 12-9. I-F alignment with signal generator and vtvm.

The time it takes to align a complete i-f section depends greatly on the skill of the technician and on the type of generator used. If the generator has sufficient output, at least 0.1 volt rms, then it can be connected to the last i-f stage input directly. If the generator has insufficient output, it may have to be connected to the first or second stage input and the tuned circuits of these stages will have to be temporarily shunted with a 1000-ohm resistor to reduce their tuning effect. Once the last stage is tuned for maximum vtvm reading at the prescribed frequencies, the output of the generator is reduced and the next stage, going toward the tuner, can be aligned.

When the agc-controlled stages are adjusted, the agc bias must be disabled. This is usually done by connecting a −3 or −1½ volt battery directly across the bias bus.

As the signal generator is connected closer to the r-f tuner, its output must be reduced so that the video detector does not overload. Generally, more than 3 volts at the vtvm represent overload; this can be checked by varying the generator amplitude and noting a corresponding increase and decrease at the vtvm. Overloading is indicated when an increase in generator output does not increase the vtvm reading. Another possibility to watch for is oscillation, which also causes the detector to saturate and will obscure tuning efforts. Often, a poorly-shielded or ungrounded signal generator lead will cause oscillation. At the first i-f stage and at the mixer grid, the overall i-f gain may be so great that a direct physical connection to the set is not necessary. Many manufacturers suggest that a loop or an insulated tube shield act as coupling from the generator directly into the mixer tube.

After each of the tuned circuits has been adjusted for maximum vtvm reading, set the generator to the trap frequencies (usually 41.25 and 47.75 mc) and tune the respective traps for minimum vtvm reading. To check the overall alignment, tune the generator from 41.25 mc slowly through the entire frequency response and observe the vtvm readings at different frequencies. At about 42 to 42.5 mc there should be a peak and a second slight peak should occur at about 45 mc. Between these two peaks, the response should not drop by less than 15%. This means that, if the peaks correspond to 3 volts on the vtvm, the valley between the two 3-volt peaks should not be less than 2.55 volts. Both peaks should be approximately the same voltage level and the 45.75-mc picture carrier should be about half-way down from the peak (about 1.5 volts in the 3-volts peak example). The response at the 41.25-mc and 47.75-mc dips should be no more than the residual d-c voltage at the video detector with the generator removed. If a generator with a calibrated attenuator is available, the generator output at the trap frequencies can be increased until the vtvm reads the same as for the peaks. The attenuator setting, in db, or in microvolts, is then a measure of the difference between the peaks and the trap frequency amplitudes.

Alignment with Sweep Generator and Oscilloscope

When a sweep generator and oscilloscope are available, the i-f alignment becomes much simpler. The sweep generator is a signal generator that is electronically tuned over the desired frequency range. This tuning, back and forth, occurs at a 60-cps rate, the same rate at which the horizontal sweep of the oscilloscope operates. Since the horizontal sweep in many sweep generators is a sine wave from the 60-cps power line, the oscilloscope sweep waveform must be the same sine wave. Some oscilloscopes already have this feature built-in, and all TV sweep generators provide a horizontal sweep output which is connected to the oscilloscope, either as synchronism or as actual sweep signal.

The oscilloscope picture now contains a graph in which, at a 60-cycle rate, the horizontal axis represents frequency and the vertical axis represents the gain of the i-f amplifiers. Normally, the video detector output is connected to the vertical scope terminal, as illustrated in Figure 12-10. The vertical scope gain controls the amplitude of the response curve and can be set so that the peaks fall into convenient slots of the scope scale. While actual amplitudes can be measured by using the scope's vertical calibration, only relative amplitudes are required for most alignment

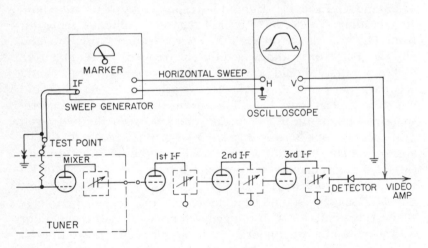

Fig. 12-10. I-F alignment with sweep generator and oscilloscope.

jobs. Most manufacturers recommend a fixed battery bias voltage as substitute for the agc bias, as explained above for the first alignment method. For sweep-generator alignment, the generator output is usually connected either to a special test point on the tuner, the mixer grid through an isolating resistor, or the signal is coupled into the mixer tube through an insulated tube shield slipped over the mixer tube. Now it is necessary only to identify the important frequencies on the response curve and then each of the stages can be aligned. Marker signals are usually available in the sweep generator as crystal oscillator signals mixed in with the sweep frequencies. They appear as pips or birdies superimposed on the response curve as in the scope photograph of Figure 12-11.

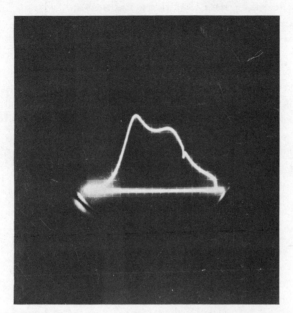

Fig. 12-11. Marker signals on the oscilloscope i-f response curve.

Different sweep generators offer different systems. One of the widely-used generators has several crystal frequencies, such as 41.25, 42, 45.75, and 47.75 mc, individually selectable by a switch. Another generator has a 4.5-mc marker that appears at 45 mc, its tenth harmonic, and a 2.5-mc marker that can be set over the 45-mc one to show 42.5 and 47.5 mc. Still another marker is then used to denote all 0.1-mc intervals. By manipulating these markers, it is possible to pick out almost any desired frequency.

In using the sweep generator method, it is not necessary to align each resonant circuit exactly for a particular frequency. They need only be adjusted for the best response curve at that general frequency range. It is possible to trim up individual stages to get a reasonably flat, evenly peaked response curve. Trap adjustments and their effect on the overall curve can be observed and other coils can be trimmed up to compensate where necessary. The interaction between two windings on a transformer can be observed and each side can be peaked for best overall response curve. In spite of the apparent simplicity of this method, the alignment frequencies for each stage should be maintained and no effort made to change them, even though the response curve still looks correct. Remember that with agc action, the response curve might change unless the correct balance is maintained.

The need to follow manufacturer's data in all cases cannot be overstressed. Trick circuits and their peculiarities are not always apparent from diagrams, but the manufacturer's service department has aligned many receivers of each particular model and usually has good reasons for specifying each frequency. We have shown that alignment of the i-f section requires a fair amount of special test equipment, which may tempt some readers to try and perform some alignment steps by using only the TV signal off the air. This invariably results in misalignment. Aligning a TV i-f section is a job for the professional. He cannot be expected to work without the proper tools.

REVIEW QUESTIONS

1. If the video i-f carrier is at 45.75 mc, what is the video frequency of a 44-mc i-f signal?
2. What type of defect is caused by inoperative or misaligned 41.25-mc traps?
3. Name the three types of traps used in TV i-f systems.
4. How are bifilar transformers aligned as compared to those having separate windings?
5. What is the purpose of R9 in the circuit of Figure 12-7?
6. What type of trap is L2-C2 in Figure 12-7?
7. What type of transistor circuit is used in all three stages of Figure 12-8?
8. Name three picture symptoms caused by i-f defects.
9. What is done with the agc bias during i-f alignment?
10. In the sweep generator alignment method, which scope axis represents frequency?

TV TUNERS

Every superheterodyne receiver has a tuning section that selects the r-f signal and converts it down to the i-f for amplification. We already know that television is transmitted over 82 different channels that fall into three separate frequency bands. Each of these channels is 6-mc wide and contains both sound and picture information. The tuner must select the desired channel, amplify a 6-mc wide band, and convert this r-f signal to the i-f with considerable accuracy in regard to the exact i-f value of the sound and picture carrier. At the same time, the tuner must provide sufficient selectivity to reject adjacent channels, as well as all sorts of interference. Because of the high frequencies used in all television channels, only line-of-sight reception is normally reliable; for most locations outside metropolitan areas external antennas are required. Again, because of the frequencies involved, impedance matching between the antenna, transmission line, and receiver is essential and is another tuner function. Phase angle differences of the r-f signal are of little importance in sound communications, but in television such effects appear as reflections or "ghosts" in the picture and must be avoided. Because these ghosts can be due to reflections or impedance mismatch in the antenna and transmission line, proper impedance of the tuner is a critical feature of its input circuits.

When we consider that the 6-mc bandwidth, uniform conversion gain, and impedance matching must be maintained from channel 2 at 54–60 mc up to channel 83 at 884–890 mc, we can see that television tuners might be very complex. Actually, most tuners do not handle this entire range of frequencies in a single tuning arrangement, but deal with it in sections. The vhf television range, channels 2–13, is usually covered by a tuner in 12 separate steps; the uhf band, channels 14–83, is covered by another tuner portion as a continuous band. Since early in 1964, all newly manufactured television receivers are required by the FCC to cover all 82 channels; before that time the majority of sets contained only 12-channel vhf tuners with a separate adapter for the uhf channels. Since almost 50 million sets are installed with a basic vhf tuner, the operation of typical 12-channel tuners will be discussed first and then the uhf tuners will be taken up. Finally, we will describe the troubleshooting and alignment principles applicable to all types of tuners.

BASIC TUNER CIRCUITS

Figure 13-1 shows the basic elements of any TV tuner. The signal is brought from the antenna by the transmission line to the input network, which contains the impedance matching and frequency selection functions. In some tuners the input network is broadly tuned, but in many models it contains a resonant circuit that is switched for each channel. The r-f amplifier stage provides

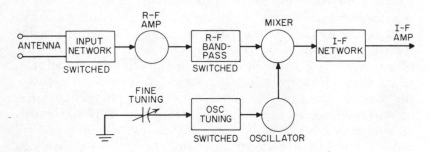

Fig. 13-1. Basic tuner elements.

some gain and, at its output, further frequency selection. This r-f bandpass network has a bandwidth of about 6 mc and helps reject adjacent channels and other undesired signals. It is invariably switched for each channel. The mixer stage uses its nonlinear characteristic to heterodyne the incoming r-f signal with the local oscillator frequency generated by the oscillator stage. To cover the required frequency range, the oscillator tuning network is also switched and, to get the exact i-f for the picture and sound carrier, a fine tuning adjustment is often provided. Finally, the

selected i-f signal is amplified at the output of the mixer and supplied to the first stage of the i-f amplifier section.

UHF Tuner Differences. This basic circuit is found in all tuners,
but in the uhf tuner sections the amplification features are omitted
because tubes capable of amplifying these high frequencies are
quite expensive. Another uhf tuner difference is that the tuned
networks are usually not switched for each channel; continuous
tuning is used instead, similar to that in broadcast and FM receivers. The vhf channels range from 54 to 216 mc, a range of 4:1,
while the uhf band extends from 470 to 890 mc, which is only a
2:1 frequency range. This latter range lends itself to the use of
so-called distributed constants or transmission line tuning, a principle discussed in more detail in the paragraphs devoted to uhf
tuning.

Television tuners are always separate subassemblies, often
manufactured by specialized manufacturers and installed in the
main chassis by the television set manufacturer. In general, both
vhf and uhf tuners have separate tuning shafts, adjustments, and
alignment points and are replaceable as entire units.

A Typical VHF Tuner

Figure 13-2 shows a typical vhf tuner. The two tubes contain all
three tube functions because the mixer and local oscillator use
separate sections of a dual tube, while the r-f amplifier invariably
is a separate tube. In the illustration, the two terminals for the
balanced 300-ohm transmission line from the antenna are clearly
shown. The inner tuning shaft performs the channel-switching and
the concentric outer shaft provides the fine-tuning adjustment.
Alignment screws for some of the tuned circuits are visible on the
top of the chassis. To avoid spurious reception of unwanted signals,
all tuner parts, including the tubes, are shielded. This also helps
to reduce radiation from the local oscillator that could cause interference with other TV sets or communication receivers.

Two basic types of vhf tuner are on the market, the *switch* and
the *turret tuner*. In switch-type tuners, the channel selector acts
like a rotary switch; it selects portions of a series of tuned elements. This means that for channel 11 the tuning elements of
channel 13 and 12 are in series with those of channel 11. The
second type of tuner is called a turret tuner because all resonant
circuits are mounted on a revolving drum, or turret, and each
channel contains a complete and independent set of tuning circuits
for that channel only.

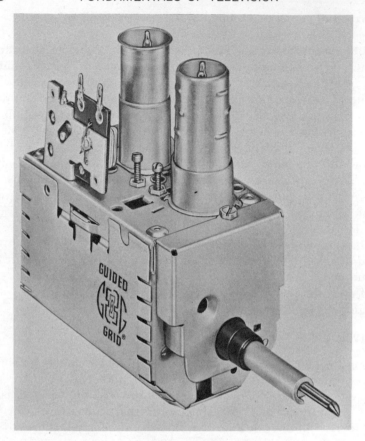

Fig. 13-2. A typical vhf tuner. (Zenith)

SWITCH TUNERS

While the actual circuits and adjustments vary among different manufacturers, the switch-type tuner circuit of Figure 13-3 is typical. The input transformer, T101, converts the balanced 300-ohm signal from the transmission line into an unbalanced signal that is selected for each channel by the first switch deck. *Balanced input* means that noise pulses picked up on the transmission line will be of opposite polarity and cancel each other out.

The r-f amplifier is a special vhf tetrode which has one set of tuning coils in the grid and another set in the plate circuit. Note that the grid coils for channels 2 to 6 are loaded by R105 to get the required bandwidth. A single adjustable coil, L108, is in series

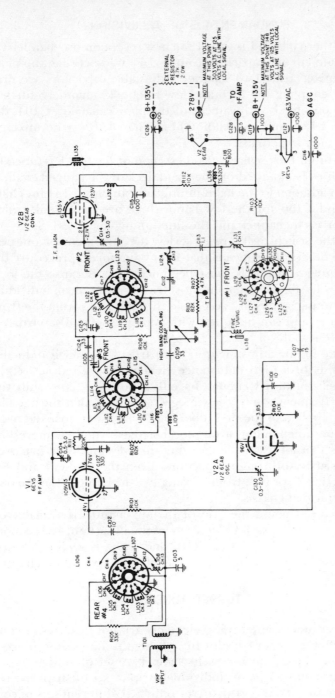

Fig. 13-3. A switch-type tuner circuit. (General Electric)

with all other coils and is tuned for best reception on channel 13. In the plate circuit, capacitive coupling is used between the plate and the mixer grid. Two separate, adjustable capacitors are provided for coupling the high and low frequency channels; further tuning is possible by adjustment of the plate capacitor, C104, the grid coil, L124, and capacitor C114. The plate of the mixer is tuned to the i-f bandpass.

In this tuner the oscillator triode section of the 6EA8 is tuned by a series of coils mounted on the front deck of the ganged channel switch. In addition to the main tuning adjustments, L131 for channel 13 and C130 for the low band, there are individual tuning screws for each channel and the fine tuning coil, L138. Since the coils on the switch deck are in series, the alignment of one will affect the others. This means that in any alignment procedure the high frequency channels must be tuned first. Because the local oscillator adjustment is the one most frequently used, all individual channel tuning screws are accessible through holes from the front of the tuner and can be tuned with a long, insulated screwdriver or alignment tool.

The fine tuning adjustment in this particular tuner is inductive and consists of a high inductance element connected across the entire oscillator-tuned circuit. Its effect, however, is to shift the oscillator frequency only a few megacycles. Note that the agc bias voltage is applied to the first tube, the r-f amplifier, to avoid overloading the tuner under strong local signals. Another interesting feature is that all leads not carrying the r-f signals are bypassed with special feed-through capacitors. Even the filament and B+ leads are thus kept free from r-f energy, which might radiate outside the shielded chassis.

A special test point, the grid of the mixer tube, is available on top of the tuner chassis for alignment of the i-f section, and another test point, isolated by resistors R107 and R110, is used to connect the oscilloscope for r-f alignment, as explained later in this chapter.

TURRET TUNERS

In turret tuners, the tuning elements are not in series; a completely different set of coils for the r-f stage and oscillator are connected into the circuit for each channel. A set of coils for each channel is mounted on an individual strip or set of strips located on a drum or turret. As the turret is turned, different sets of coils are brought into contact with the stationary switch contacts and connected into the circuit. The individual coil strips are usually removable for repair and replacement, as can be seen in Figure 13-4.

This Standard Coil tuner (Figure 13-4) is probably the most widely used model, having been incorporated in the sets of the majority of manufacturers between 1950 and 1955. The earlier version of this tuner used a pentode as r-f amplifier and a dual triode to perform the functions of mixing and local oscillator.

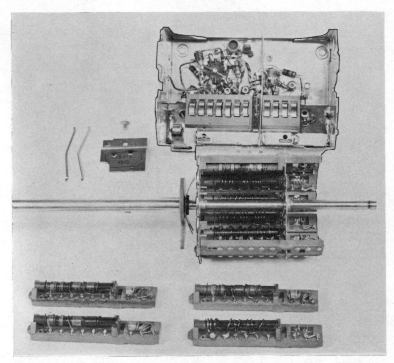

Fig. 13-4. Coil strips and turret tuner mechanism. (Standard Kollsman)

While the tube types and actual circuitry have changed, the basic turret arrangement has been used in many millions of TV tuners. The principle of the segmented turret includes the location of the oscillator coil nearest to the front of the receiver, with a hole in the chassis allowing the alignment of the local oscillator independently for each channel as that channel is tuned in.

The circuit for this widely-used tuner is shown in Figure 13-5. A 300-ohm centertapped input transformer is tuned by a resonant circuit connected across it by channel switching. A tuned trans-

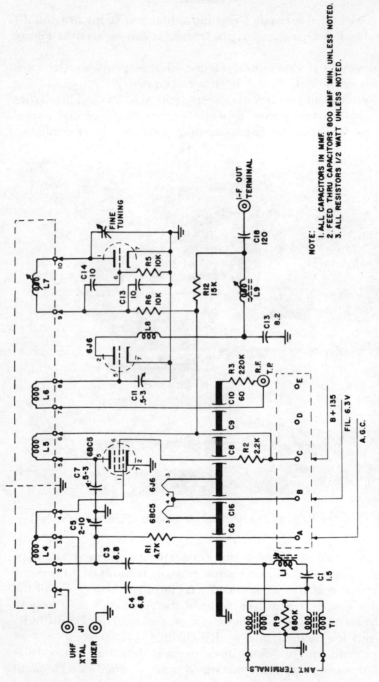

Fig. 13-5. The circuit diagram of the turret tuner shown in Fig. 13-4. (Standard Kollsman)

former switched for each channel couples the output of the r-f amplifier to the input of the mixer triode. Both of these tuned networks are designed to provide the proper 6-mc bandwidth and impedance match for the designated channel. The oscillator coil is also contained on the turret strip. In addition to the switched coils there are master trimmer capacitors in the grid and plate circuit of the r-f amplifier. Fine or "sharp" tuning is accomplished by a capacitor in the oscillator circuit that is variable by rotation of the outer concentric tube of the turret tuner shaft. The output of the mixer is tuned to the i-f bandpass.

A single coil segment is shown in Figures 13-4 and 13-5, but earlier turret tuners used two coil segments. Another type, the Admiral model illustrated in Figure 13-6, is further simplified

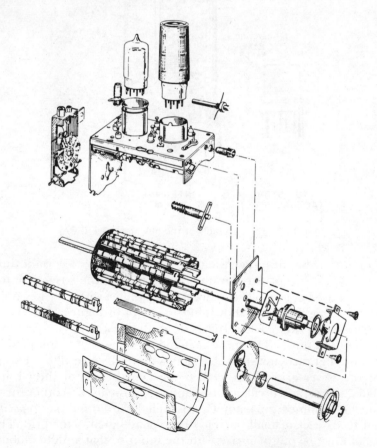

Fig. 13-6. A single strip turret tuner. (Admiral)

in that the coil strip also serves as mandrel for all coils. This provides some economy over earlier models where separate coil forms are used that are then mounted on the contact segments.

The Nuvistor. One of the most recent developments in tuners is the use of an entirely new type of tube, the nuvistor. This tube features a unique construction that permits very close and accurate spacing of the tube elements, resulting in a relatively inexpensive, vhf amplifier tube with excellent electrical and mechanical characteristics. In the cutaway view of Figure 13-7, this novel construction can be clearly seen.

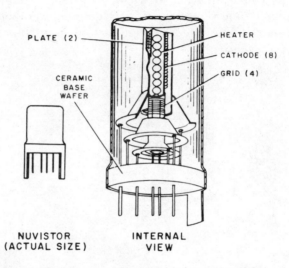

PLATE (2)   HEATER
CATHODE (8)
GRID (4)
CERAMIC
BASE
WAFER

NUVISTOR   INTERNAL
(ACTUAL SIZE)   VIEW

Fig. 13-7. The assembly of the nuvistor tube. (RCA)

In outward appearance the tube is quite similar to certain transistor types, except for the number of pins in the base. The nuvistor is used as a stabilized triode r-f amplifier with very low noise and very high gain, as shown in the circuit of Figure 13-8, which illustrates the RCA KRK 102A turret tuner, a very compact and efficient vhf tuner. The input matching transformer is followed by a multiple-tuned network that acts as interference filter. Except for the series grid-tuning coil, the switched coils for the r-f amplifier, mixer, and oscillator are similar to those used in other turret tuners. Trimmer capacitor C21 is called the *neutralizing capacitor* and feeds back a small portion of the plate signal to the grid. This signal must be out of phase with the input so that a slight amount of degeneration occurs to prevent any instability that might lead

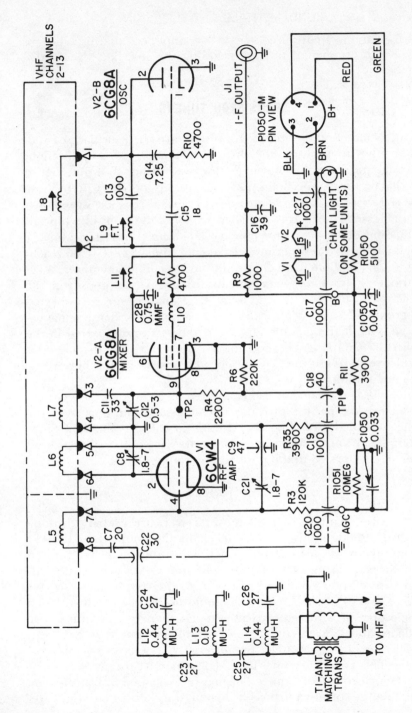

Fig. 13-8. Nuvistor turret tuner circuit. (RCA)

to oscillation. Neutralized triode r-f amplifiers of this type are used in a number of tuners, including the so-called "Neutrode" tuners.

TRANSISTOR TUNERS

As in many other circuits, transistors are used in place of vacuum tubes to perform the three functions of r-f amplification, mixing, and local oscillator in the transistor tuner shown in Figure 13-9. The tuning mechanism of this tuner is a turret with individual coil strips for each vhf channel. Because this tuner is used on a portable set, a switch is provided to select the built-in whip antenna or connect to a conventional 300-ohm transmission line. A high-pass filter prevents lower frequency interference from reaching the r-f amplifier, which is connected as common emitter. As in a triode r-f amplifier, a small neutralizing capacitor goes from the collector to the base tuned circuit. The mixer stage is connected as grounded base circuit with the r-f and local oscillator signal being mixed at the emitter input and the i-f tuning located in the collector. Coupling between the r-f amplifier and the mixer is inductive, through the two coils located next to each other on the channel tuning strip.

The local oscillator is also connected as grounded base circuit. A feedback capacitor provides the necessary coupling from the collector tuned circuit to the emitter to cause oscillation. Since all transistors are p-n-p types, all collectors are returned to ground and all emitters go to the positive B+ source.

UHF TUNERS

To cover channels 14 to 83, most receivers use a separate tuning circuit, although this is often mechanically coupled to the vhf tuning controls on the front panel. The tuning mechanism and the electrical principles of these uhf tuners are sufficiently different to deserve separate discussion. At the frequencies used for uhf, 470–890 mc, ordinary coils would be reduced to less than a single turn of wire and capacitors to less than 10 picofarads. The stability and adjustment of these parameters would be very difficult to control accurately. Because the wavelength is so short, it is possible to use tuned lines instead of coils and capacitors.

The principle of the tuned line may be explained by transmission line theory. For our purpose it is enough to know that at uhf fre-

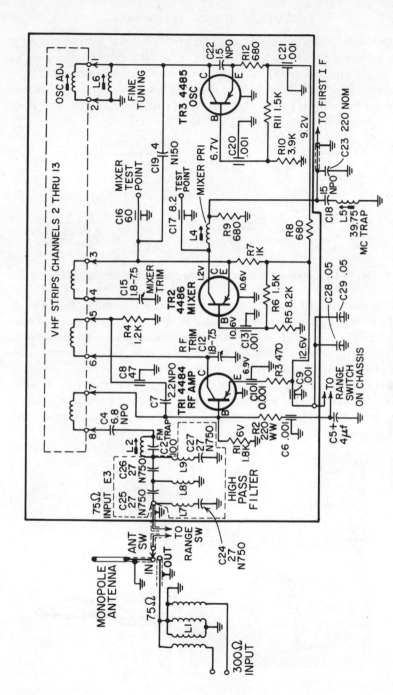

Fig. 13-9. VHF transistor tuner circuit. (Motorola)

quencies the inductance of a straight piece of metal is large enough
to permit use of the metal line as a coiled wire. At the end of such
a strip, or line, is a capacitor that determines the exact resonant frequency. Figure 13-10 illustrates the difference between a resonant
network of lumped constants and one of distributed constants. The
latter is usually found in uhf tuners.

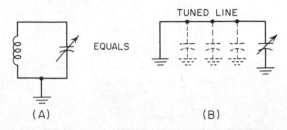

Fig. 13-10. Lumped constants (A) and distributed constants (B).

Because the uhf band tunes over such a wide range, the tuning
dial or shaft is geared down to allow proper tuning for each of the
70 uhf channels. This is similar to the dial and string mechanism
or planetary drives used in communications receivers and still
found in some deluxe broadcast receivers.

UHF tuners are usually very compact, as illustrated by Figure
13-11, which shows a recent tuner that has been used in conjunction with vhf tuners. Receivers that do not contain a uhf tuner can

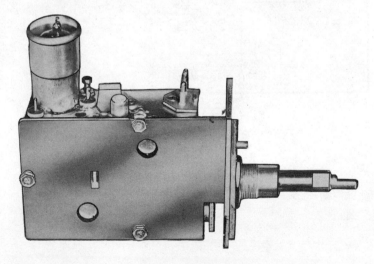

Fig. 13-11. A typical uhf tuner. (Standard Kollsman)

be used for uhf reception by adding a converter. Such a unit is simply a uhf tuner with its own power supply that is housed in a separate small cabinet. Electrically, the only difference in a uhf converter is that its output is usually tuned to an unused vhf channel, instead of directly to the i-f of the TV set. This output is connected to the vhf tuner antenna terminals.

A Typical UHF Tuner

The circuit of a typical uhf tuner is shown in Figure 13-12 and shows only a single tube—the oscillator. Oscillating either above or below the desired uhf channel, the incoming signal is converted to the 40 mc i-f, which is then fed to the vhf tuner. This latter unit has a thirteenth channel position, usually labelled UHF, in which the tuner is tuned to the 40-mc i-f band and the vhf oscillator is disabled. Thus, the vhf tuner provides extra amplification for the i-f.

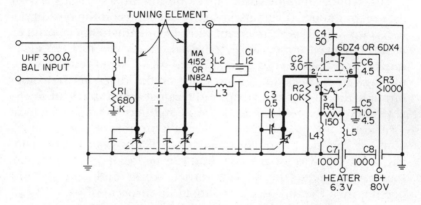

Fig. 13-12. UHF tuner circuit. (Standard Kollsman)

Tubes that amplify and tune over the uhf band are quite expensive. For this reason, a simple preselector stage is used, followed by the mixer stage, which employs a uhf diode to provide the nonlinear element needed for mixing. Note in the circuit of Figure 13-12 that the 300-ohm uhf input coil is coupled to the tuned element (heavy line) by mere proximity and that coupling between that resonant circuit and the mixer stage consists only of a window in the grounded shield compartment that separates each resonant circuit. The mixer diode is connected to a point on the mixer resonant line corresponding to proper impedance match

and similar to a tap on a coil. To couple the oscillator signal into
the mixer, a small loop is passed into the oscillator compartment.
L2 and L3, together with the feed-through capacitor, C1, act as a
filter to remove the uhf beat signals and pass only the i-f band to
the coaxial connector at the end of L2.

The location of the various connections and, especially, all
ground points is quite critical and any changes will seriously
alter the frequency and the performance of the uhf circuits. Note
that the oscillator tube has dual grid and plate leads, which helps
reduce the inherent lead inductance of the tube itself. The tube
also is well-shielded and uses a special low-capacitance tube socket.
All filament and power leads are carefully decoupled at the point
where they enter the tuner chassis.

ALIGNMENT AND TROUBLESHOOTING

The troubleshooting procedure for all tuners, regardless of
type or frequency coverage, invariably depends on the type of defect. Two main types can occur. Most frequently neither sound or
picture, or even noise, can be received on any channel. To make
certain that the tuner is at fault, feed an i-f signal into the first
i-f stage and check for its presence at the detector. If it goes
through the i-f section, advance the signal generator lead to the
vhf tuner mixer test point. If the i-f still gets through, the local
oscillator is the most likely culprit. Tube trouble or poor connections are the most frequent cause for oscillator failure. Occasionally, a broken wire or poor ground can be located as the trouble
source. Of course, if the vhf portion works and only the uhf
doesn't, then the uhf oscillator should be suspected first.

If the oscillator works, then it should be possible to inject an
r-f signal of the proper channel frequency at the test point, or
even at the antenna terminal, that should go through to the detector. Here, it is possible to observe if the signal goes as far as the
test point or if the r-f amplifier itself is defective. In actual practice,
the most likely defect will be either the oscillator stage or the tuning mechanism. The latter is a source of most intermittent troubles
because of the many possibilities of poor contact in the switching
mechanism. To make sure that this source is eliminated it is good
practice, whenever a set has to be removed from the cabinet for
service, to treat the tuner contacts with a good contact cleaner.

A number of preparations are on the market that contain a cleaning as well as a lubricating agent and can be applied conveniently through spray cans or with some injection mechanism that reaches the tight spots in the switching area.

To align tuners, either a sweep generator and oscilloscope or a signal generator and vtvm are necessary. The latter method is not very handy and should only be used for temporary alignment. Figure 13-13 shows the connection used for a sweep generator and oscilloscope. When a balanced 300-ohm generator is used, the matching pad is not needed. The oscilloscope vertical input can be isolated by means of the 10,000-ohm resistor shown or else a probe

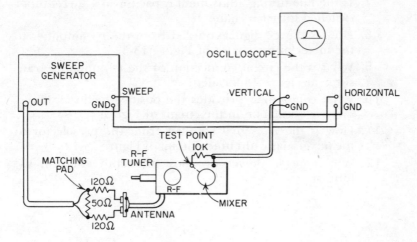

Fig. 13-13. R-F tuner alignment with sweep generator and oscilloscope.

using some isolation can be used. In many tuners the isolation is already built-in and the scope can be connected directly to the test point. The response curve should be about 6 mc between peaks with no more than a 15% valley. Since the gain of the tuner is much less than that provided in the i-f section, the response curve at the r-f is not so critical, but it should be wide and even enough to allow all frequencies within the 6-mc channel to reach the i-f section with less than 15% reduction. The response curve of color receivers is slightly more critical. Manufacturer's instructions should be followed carefully in making each alignment and adjustment step.

Review Questions

1. What are the three basic tuner stages?
2. What are the vhf and uhf television frequency bands?
3. Name two reasons for shielding the TV tuner stages?
4. Why does the alignment of channel 12 affect channel 10 in a switch-type tuner?
5. Which channels are aligned by adjustment of C104 in Figure 13-3?
6. To what approximate frequency will L135 in Figure 13-3 be tuned?
7. Is the fine tuning adjustment capacitor in a turret tuner switched for each channel?
8. How is the r-f signal coupled from the r-f amplifier to the mixer in the circuit of Figure 13-5?
9. What is the circuit connection of the r-f amplifier transistor in Figure 13-9 called?
10. What component provides the positive feedback necessary for oscillation in the circuit of Figure 13-9?
11. How is the r-f signal coupled from the preselector to the mixer in the uhf tuner circuit of Figure 13-12?
12. What types of defects are most frequently found in TV tuners?

TV ANTENNAS AND TRANSMISSION LINES

Broadcast and communications receivers operate from such relatively simple antennas as the familiar built-in loop or, simply, long wires mounted vertically or horizontally, depending on the polarization of the signal. As long as only sound is received we are not too concerned with r-f phase differences due to reflections because they cannot be heard. In television receivers, however, such reflections cause visible ghosts in the picture, which can become a quite severe problem. Also, in television, each channel that is to be received has a relatively broad bandpass. All in all, television antennas are much more critical than those used in other services.

Desired Antenna Properties. Television signals are transmitted either on the vhf or the uhf band, which means that they are not reflected by the ionosphere and only line-of-sight reception is reliable. On the other hand, reflections from hills, buildings, or even airplanes cause trouble because the reflected signal often arrives at the antenna slightly behind the straight-line signal, causing ghosts to appear in the picture. The attenuation of the atmosphere is much greater at the higher frequencies, so receivers located far from the transmitter will get weak signals mixed in with noise. To overcome all this, the television antenna must often have considerable gain and to utilize this gain, exact impedance matching between the antenna and the receiver is important. To sum up, TV antennas must have the required bandwidth, correct impedance over the entire band, and gain and directivity to eliminate unwanted reflections.

To achieve all of these properties, TV antennas must be tuned. We know that the vhf band is divided into two groups of channels and, therefore, vhf antennas are generally available specially tuned for these two bands. For uhf, the antenna is usually tuned some-where in the center of the 470–890-mc band. Some uhf antennas are designed to cover just a few channels in the uhf band with especially good gain or directivity. Antennas are tuned by their length, as will be explained below, which means that the antennas for the low vhf band are much longer than those for the high vhf or the uhf band. This also means that uhf antennas can be more elaborate, since their overall structure is smaller.

PRINCIPLE OF THE DIPOLE

Resonant circuits can take either of two forms. The so-called *lumped constants circuits* consist of a coil and a capacitor, as found in the r-f and i-f circuits of the TV receiver. The second form is generally called a *distributed constants circuit* and depends on the co-incidence of the physical length of the element and the wavelength of the signal. Figure 14-1 illustrates the simplest form of resonant

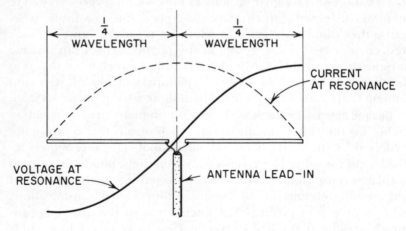

Fig. 14-1. A simple dipole antenna.

antenna, the *half-wave dipole*. If a metal rod is cut to half the wave-length of a particular signal, the current at resonance will be maxi-mum at the center and zero at each end. At the same time, the volt-age will be maximum but of opposite polarity at either end. Now, if the rod is cut at the center, two quarter-wavelength elements re-main and the center maximum current can be tapped off to drive the receiver input. Theoretically, the impedance at the exact center is zero, accounting for the maximum current and zero voltage. For practical reasons, the transmission line to the receiver is connected near the center, at a point where the impedance is of some suitable value, such as 300 ohms, in television. The actual distance from the center and the precise impedance at any point depend on the ratio of the diameter of the element to its length.

Dipole antennas are used in many other services as well. In television they often are used in conjunction with other configurations, but the basic antenna is the same. A single-tuned dipole is considered to have 0 db gain, meaning that it serves as standard for measuring the gain of other antenna types. If we read that an antenna has a gain of 3 db, we know that it will pick up twice as much r-f power as a tuned dipole. All antenna gain figures indicate how much more gain a particular type has than its equivalent dipole.

Directivity

The directivity of an antenna is described by an imaginary line surrounding the antenna from which equal power signals would be received with equal signal strength. An omnidirectional antenna has a directivity pattern that is a circle with the antenna at its center. Simple tuned dipoles have the directivity pattern shown in Figure 14-2, which indicates that maximum signal pick-up can be expected from either front or back, but practically no signal will be picked up from the ends of the elements. When a reflector, such as a large metal sheet, is placed behind the dipole, no signal will be picked up from that direction (Figure 14-3). If the reflector is placed a quarter-wavelength behind the dipole and parallel to it, signals reaching the reflector will be reflected to the dipole, improving its gain from the forward direction. Instead of a metal sheet, a single rod, slightly longer than the dipole, can be placed a quarter-wavelength behind the dipole as the reflector. If we place another rod that is a little shorter than the dipole in front of the dipole, it will act as a director by picking up signals and directing them to the dipole itself.

Once a reflector or a director, or both, have been added to a dipole, the gain, bandwidth, and directivity are no longer the same. Gain and directivity increase, together with the amount of reflections and direction, but the bandwidth decreases. Antenna designers can space director and reflector elements in different combinations to achieve a host of different characteristics. Many of the high-gain, multichannel antennas consist of such complex combinations. Bandwidth and impedance must be carefully considered in such designs.

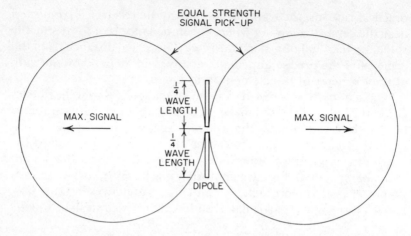

Fig. 14-2. The directivity pattern of a simple tuned dipole.

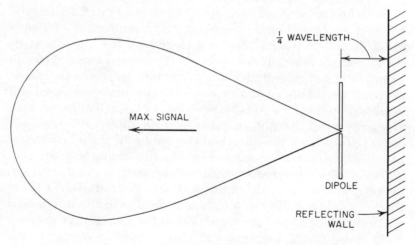

Fig. 14-3. The directivity pattern of a dipole and reflector.

ANTENNA ARRAYS

In weak signal areas it is common practice to use several antennas in parallel to get enough signal pick-up. Usually, two or four sets of antennas, each with a reflector and a number of directors, are mounted above each other, as shown in Figure 14-4. If we connect two 300-ohm antennas in parallel, the total impedance will be 150 ohms, and, if the antennas are close together, they will interfere

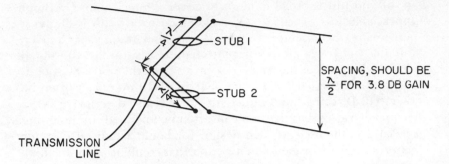

Fig. 14-4. Stacked antennas.

with each other. For this reason, certain definite rules must be
followed when stacking antennas. For one thing, the two antennas
should be far enough apart to eliminate interference and to get the
maximum benefit of the stacking. At a spacing of a half-wavelength,
the gain due to stacking will be 3.8 db, or a doubling of the received power. As the antennas are brought closer this advantage
decreases, until, at a quarter-wavelength, only 1 db gain is obtained.

To get proper impedance match, the stacking bars must be one
or three quarter-wavelengths long and must have the right characteristic impedance. The characteristic impedance of stacking
bars, like any transmission line, depends on the diameter and the
spacing of the conductors. Stacking bars are the transmission-line
equivalent of a transformer. The stacking bar characteristic impedance should be the square root of the product of the input and
output impedance. The characteristic impedance of any two-
conductor, balanced line is equal to 276 times the log of the ratio
of twice the conductor spacing divided by the conductor diameter.
Since stacking bars and transmission lines are commercially available items, the reader will rarely have a chance to use these formu-
las, but he will know that the manufacturer's instructions on stacking antennas must be followed exactly.

TYPES OF ANTENNAS

While the basic dipole is the standard of measurement for antenna gain, a host of variations of the dipole have been developed,
many especially for use in television installations. As we have
shown, the dipole is tuned to a single frequency, but its bandwidth

at vhf and uhf is broad enough to cover a 6-mc channel without appreciable loss of signal strength. Since bandwidth is always a percentage of the center frequency, at higher frequencies a given antenna will cover more adjacent channels. Naturally, the signal pick-up drops off as the frequency varies from the resonance point, but in strong signal areas even a drop of 10 times can often be tolerated. Directivity and impedance match also deteriorate as the frequency varies, but that too can often be tolerated. In designing special TV antennas, we can design for better bandwidth, or for better directivity or gain. An antenna that combines a lot of these features is usually not one but several antennas arranged in some kind of combination.

Folded Dipole

The first variation of the dipole is a *folded dipole,* shown in Figure 14-5, which provides slightly higher gain than a dipole and gives a broader frequency response with better 300-ohm impedance. If the diameter and spacing of the folded dipole are designed for

Fig. 14-5. A folded dipole with a reflector.

300-ohms characteristic impedance, it will retain this impedance over a very broad frequency band. Directivity of a folded dipole is the same as that for a basic dipole.

Conical Antenna

Shown in Figure 14-6 is a simple *conical antenna* made up of two V elements, slanted forward towards the transmitter. This type of antenna is characterized by fairly good gain and excellent bandwidth. In uhf the two V sections can be made into a solid sheetmetal wedge or into a hollow cone, with even better bandwidth characteristics.

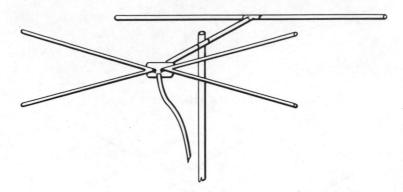

Fig. 14-6. A conical antenna with a reflector.

Double V Antenna

The *double V antenna,* a popular design, depends on the angles and on the distance between front and back elements for its gain, directivity, and bandwidth. A double V type is usually sufficiently broadband to cover high and low vhf bands and has as much directivity as a basic dipole with a reflector. As shown in Figure 14-7, the ends of the V are aimed toward the transmitter.

Yagi

Named after its Japanese inventor, the *Yagi antenna* (Figure 14-8) uses either a basic dipole or a folded dipole together with a reflector and two or more director elements. The Yagi antenna is distinguished by its high gain, at least 6 db or more, and its excellent directivity. A simple Yagi has a rather narrow bandwidth

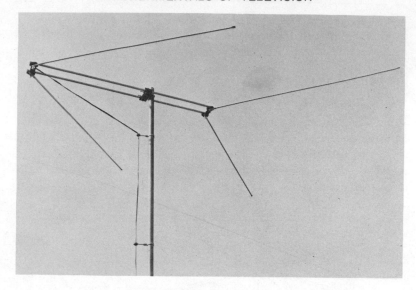

Fig. 14-7. A double V antenna (JFD Corp)

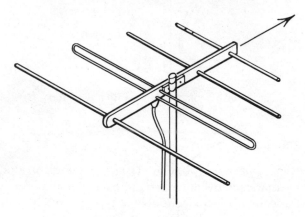

Fig. 14-8. A Yagi antenna.

because each element is tuned only to the center frequency. Modified Yagi antennas have been built which combine elements of different length to provide broader frequency response.

UHF Antennas

Basically any vhf type can be used as a uhf antenna, with the elements properly shortened to resonate in the uhf band. Because the wavelengths are so much shorter, it is possible to build more elaborate structures, such as the "bow tie" or conical antenna with the corner reflector shown in Figure 14-9. Special uhf types include circular loops and rhombic- or diamond-shaped antennas. The latter are highly directional and have the same high gain characteristics of the larger rhombic antennas used for commercial communication links. Because of greater propagation losses and reflection problems, uhf antennas must usually perform much better than their vhf counterparts. For this reason, special care must be given to the selection and installation of uhf antennas.

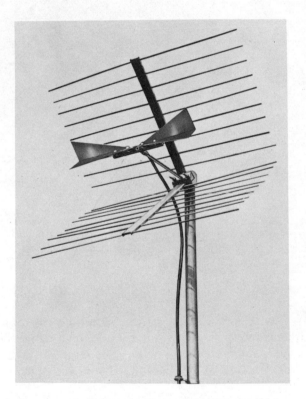

Fig. 14-9. A uhf conical antenna.

Indoor and Built-In Antennas

Almost every TV set is now equipped with "rabbit ears," the V-oriented, basic dipole antenna. Its characteristics are those of a basic dipole. This means that for optimum performance on one channel, its length should be adjusted for that channel. As shown

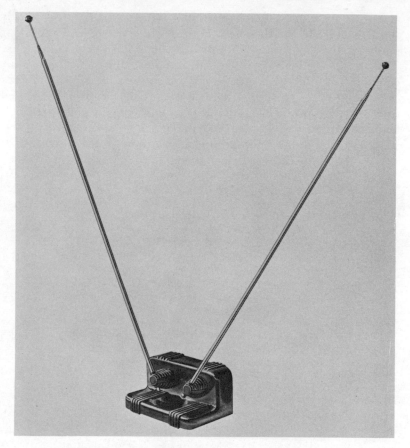

Fig. 14-10. A rabbit ears antenna. (Ward Corp.)

in Figure 14-10, each element can be separately tilted and pulled out. It will be necessary to experiment by extending both elements to the same length and then rotating the entire assembly for the best possible picture. The elements should be as close to horizontal and as high as possible.

Indoor antennas suffer from changes in signal as people walk around a room, as metal blinds are closed, and so on. Their efficiency depends on the construction of the house and its orientation with regard to the TV transmitter. Antennas built into the TV receiver cabinet are generally useful only in very good signal locations. They tend to suffer from reflections and the resulting ghosts on the screen, as well as from signal fading as their surroundings are changed by people moving about, etc.

TRANSMISSION LINES

You are most likely familiar with the flat, ribbon-like TV transmission lines that can be seen wherever a TV antenna is connected to a receiver. This transmission line has a characteristic impedance of 300 ohms designed to match the balanced input of TV receivers to the balanced antenna. Neither side of the 300-ohm line is connected to ground, so care must be taken against accidental grounding which would unbalance the line and cause signal losses. When installing 300-ohm line, it is important to keep the line at least a few inches from a grounded surface and any long metal areas, such as drain pipes.

Transmission lines can be considered to be a series of inductances shunted by a series of capacitances, which means that resonances can occur. As long as both ends of a transmission line are terminated in its characteristic impedance (300 ohms for TV lines), this causes no trouble, but if a mismatch occurs at either the TV tuner or at the antenna, then resonance effects or "standing waves" can occur along the transmission line. The most objectionable of these effects are r-f reflections, because they result in a phase difference of signals at the tuner and therefore appear as ghosts in the picture. To determine if ghosts are caused by the transmission line, it is only necessary to grasp the line firmly and slide your hand up and down, observing the picture. If the ghosts change, the transmission line reflections are causing them. A simple remedy is either to trim the transmission-line length until it is effectively some multiple of a quarter-wavelength, or else wrap a piece of metal foil about 6 inches wide around the line and move it up and down for the best picture.

In installations where excessive noise is present, special, shielded 300-ohm line can be used. This transmission line is more expensive and requires that the outer jacket be carefully grounded at the receiver. Another type of 300-ohm transmission line has been especially designed for uhf that consists of a polyethylene tube with the conductors embedded in the tubing. In some types, the tubing is filled with plastic foam while in others it is empty. These special shapes help confine the r-f fields between the two conductors and thereby reduce the outside signal losses.

The Balun. In certain specialized applications, the transmission line to the TV set will be a 75-ohm or 56-ohm coaxial cable. This requires that a transformation device, usually called a *balun*, be used to transform from balanced to unbalanced impedance and from 300 ohm to the lower impedance. If such a transformer is not used, considerable signal loss must be expected and reflections, with resultant ghosts in the picture, may be unavoidable.

MULTIPLE TV SET CONNECTIONS

With many homes owning two or more TV receivers, the problem of driving two sets from a single antenna has become quite frequent. We know from the previous discussion of transmission lines and antenna impedances that simply paralleling leads will result in considerable mismatch and signal loss. Commercially available multicouplers, such as the one shown in Figure 14-11, use r-f transformers and careful impedance matching to minimize signal losses and maintain good balance at all three sets of

Fig. 14-11. A multicoupler. (Brach Antenna Corp.)

terminals. It should be realized, however, that without amplification the maximum signal available at the antenna will ideally be split into two parts, one half of the total r-f power going to each receiver. Where many receivers are to be supplied by a single antenna, amplification must be provided before the signals are divided up.

Master Antenna Installations. In apartment houses, master antenna installations are very popular. Here, a set of high-quality antennas, carefully oriented for best reception, feeds signals to a set of r-f amplifiers that drives cables going to each tenant. These cables are usually coaxial and have 50 ohms impedance. A simple resistance network is often used in the wall outlet to get from the 50-ohm unbalanced to 300-ohm balanced impedance. Master antenna systems are basically the same as community antenna systems. These systems are installed and serviced by men who are specialists in this field of television (essentially they are television technicians who have concentrated on r-f techniques).

There are many areas where extra-sensitive antennas are required and where high-gain installations or antenna preamplifiers are used. Anyone familiar with electronics who has an understanding of television can install these devices simply by following the manufacturer's instructions. (Another aspect of antennas is antenna rotators and their controls; these are considered in Chapter 21.)

TROUBLESHOOTING

Antennas and their transmission lines usually fail only in simple mechanical ways. Wind and weather are the greatest causes of trouble, so troubleshooting is confined mostly to visual checks and occasional ohmmeter testing. Antenna and transmission line trouble appears in the TV set in the form of weak pictures that are frequently unstable, with noise, which appears as snow, obscuring the picture. To make sure that the defect is in the antenna system, disconnect the transmission line at the receiver and observe the effect of touching either or both terminals with a long wire or, better yet, connecting an indoor antenna. If it is apparent that the regular antenna and transmission line bring no signal to the receiver, a visual check of the antenna itself and all sections of the line is indicated. Look for broken elements and for cuts or breaks in the transmission line, especially at entry points and at the antenna terminals. Often these terminals are so corroded that only a high resistance contact exists between the line and the antenna, causing loss of signals. To check continuity of the entire system at the receiver location, an ohmmeter is connected between the two transmission-line wires. If a folded dipole is used, d-c resistance in the order of a few ohms, at most, should be measured. For other antenna types it is necessary to connect a clip lead across the two antenna elements and then check total d-c resistance. Open-circuit readings or high resistances indicate a defect; to isolate it, the measurements can be repeated at the antenna itself.

Occasionally, the orientation of the antenna with respect to the transmitter is thrown off by strong winds or by loosening of the mast mounting assembly. This can be checked by comparing antenna position with neighboring antennas and by looking at the mast assembly. Often, previous corrosion will show how the antenna had been oriented. Detailed installation instructions for particular antennas are supplied by the antenna manufacturers (a general procedure for installation will be found in Chapter 21).

Review Questions

1. List four important TV antenna characteristics.
2. How much db gain does an antenna that picks up twice as much signal power as a dipole have?
3. What is the voltage at the ends of a quarter-wavelength dipole?
4. What happens to the bandwidth of an antenna when a reflector or director element is added?
5. When several antennas are connected together, which two features are very important?
6. How does a folded dipole differ in directivity from a simple dipole?
7. What is the main feature of a conical antenna?
8. What happens if one side of a 300-ohm transmission line is grounded?
9. Name three items to check in troubleshooting antenna defects?
10. What type of picture symptoms are usually associated with the antenna and transmission line?

COLOR PICTURE TUBES

The picture tube is the heart of the color TV set, as it is in the monochrome receiver; for this reason its operation and the various signals supplied to it must be thoroughly understood. In Chapter 5 we presented the fundamentals of color television and gave a brief description of the color picture tube and its essential parts. Rather than repeat this material here, we suggest that the reader refresh his memory by turning back to Chapter 5 (in particular, Figures 5-3 and 5-4).

A more detailed view of the basic elements of the color picture tube is shown in Figure 15-1. Here we see the three electron guns in schematic symbols together with typical operating voltages. Note that the high-voltage focus element and the second anode, named *ultor* in color TV, are the only elements common to all three electron guns. The first anode or screen grid voltages are different for each color. Control grids and cathodes are separate, but in most receivers the three cathodes and filaments are connected together externally.

We know from Chapter 5 that the screen of the color picture tube consists of a dot pattern of three types of phosphors that emit green, blue, and red light, respectively, when excited by the electron beam. For each phosphor color there is a separate electron beam, originating and controlled by its respective electron gun.

All three electron beams are focused and accelerated together and they are deflected by a single magnetic deflection yoke. If we think, for a moment, of the three electron beams as three beams of colored light that must pass through one set of holes to strike a screen, we can readily see the importance of having the beams

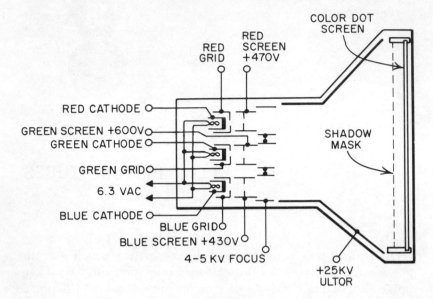

Fig. 15-1. The basic elements of the color picture tube.

converge at each of the holes in the shadow mask. (Refer back to Figure 5-4 which illustrates the convergence of the three beams at one hole.) Actually, the three beams are moved rapidly over the entire screen and must be in convergence at every hole. Needless to say, the shadow mask and the phosphor dot screen must also be perfectly aligned. This beam convergence and alignment to the dot pattern necessitates a great deal of circuitry and components not found in other picture tubes. Before discussing the unique and somewhat complex convergence circuits, the more familiar video portion will be described.

COLOR VIDEO AND D-C ADJUSTMENTS

In black-and-white picture tubes the video signal is applied either to the grid or cathode of the electron gun and the d-c bias, which determines picture brightness, is applied to the cathode or grid. In modern color receivers the electron gun also adds the Y or *brightness signal* to the chroma signal peculiar to each electron gun. We have indicated in Chapter 5 that present color transmission standards use the brightness element common to the three colors as the Y signal and transmit the hues of the colors as the difference between the brightness element and the color itself. The concept of the color difference signal will be discussed

in more detail in Chapters 16 and 17; for the moment, it is sufficient to know that at the color picture tube four signals are combined. The Y signal (brightness) is added to the $R-Y$, the red color-
difference signal, to the $G-Y$, the green color-difference signal,
and to the $B-Y$, the blue color-difference signal. This addition is
performed simply by applying the Y signal to each of the three
cathodes and the color-difference signals to the respective control
grids of the three electron guns as shown in Figure 15-2.

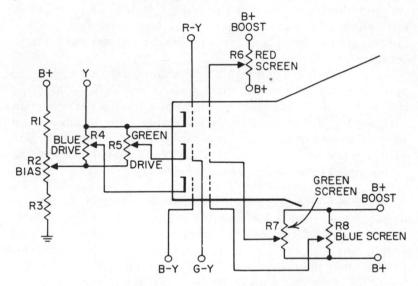

Fig. 15-2. The video and d-c color adjustments.

We know from basic colorimetry, as well as from the color
characteristic of the human eye, that the amounts of each of the
primary colors that make up white are not equal. For that reason
the amount of brightness signal applied to the red, green, and
blue electron guns must be carefully adjusted. In the circuit of
Figure 15-2, which is typical of the latest color receiver models, a
master d-c adjustment sets the overall bias for all three electron
guns, corresponding to the brightness adjustment on monochrome
picture tubes. The red brightness then serves as the basis to which
the green and blue are set to achieve a balanced "white" on the
screen. (The detailed alignment procedure at the end of this
chapter shows how each of these adjustments is made in sequence.)

On a monochrome transmission no color information is received,
the three control grids will be at some low d-c voltage, and the con-

trast, or video gain of each electron gun, is determined by the balance of R4 and R5 in Figure 15-2. The relative overall coloring of the screen, however, will depend on the red screen, R6, green screen, R7, and blue screen, R8, controls. With no video signal at all, these three controls are set to give a light, neutral grey shade. The bias control, R2, sets the brightness level of that grey, and the blue and green drive controls balance out the video amplitudes to give a good black-and-white picture. There is some interaction between these controls and the setting of the screen controls. Careful, step-by-step adjustment procedures have been worked out that are presented both at the end of this chapter and in Chapter 22.

As illustrated in Figure 15-2, the color-difference signals are applied to their respective control grids. These signals come from the color demodulator and matrix section that is the subject of Chapter 16. Here we need only know that these signals are not adjusted as part of the color picture tube circuits and that they are video signals which contain a strong blanking pulse capable of cutting the electron beam off completely during the horizontal and vertical retrace periods.

How the high voltage for the focus element and the ultor is obtained was discussed in Chapter 9 and a typical high voltage flyback circuit used in color receivers was shown in Figure 9-3. All precautions inherent in high voltage circuits apply equally for color picture tubes and the connections to them. The ultor is either the metal frame or else a metal connector at the funnel portion of the glass envelope. The focus connection is made at the picture tube base. Adjustment of the focus is done in the same manner as in monochrome sets, as the focus element is common to all three beams. In color picture tubes the focus voltage is usually between 4 and 6 kv and the potentiometer is therefore well insulated. Focus adjustments are made for average brightness, preferably with a monochrome picture or a blank, light grey screen. Adjust the focus for sharp lines over the greatest portion of the screen. A final focus adjustment can be made after all other adjustments are completed.

COLOR PURITY

It is essential that each electron beam strike only its respective color dots. Two separate steps are used in color picture tube adjustment to assure this: (1) Each individual beam is adjusted so that it converges at each of the shadow mask holes at the correct angle. For this purpose a system of convergence components is used. (2) A *purity adjustment* then assures that all three beams pass through the exact deflection center of the deflection yoke so that they are all equally deflected and line up with the holes all over the screen.

The convergence components "bundle" the three beams together and the purity components center the entire bundle on each of the holes. A purifying magnet assembly is mounted directly behind the convergence assembly on the neck of the picture tube. In appearance, the purifying magnet looks like some of the centering magnets found in certain monochrome receivers and it performs a similar function. The strength of the purifying magnet's field is adjusted by rotating two tabs towards each other. The direction of the magnetic field is determined by rotating the entire ring assembly around the neck of the picture tube. Detailed adjusting instructions are given at the end of this chapter and in Chapter 22.

One of the problems of color picture tubes is the extreme precision needed in the magnetic fields that affect the electron beams. Any extraneous magnetic field around the tube will affect the beams and prevent them from reaching their respective color dots. When color TV receivers have been shipped some distance they generally have passed through a number of magnetic fields, including variations of the earth's field, so that some residual magnetism remains in the metal structure surrounding the screen. This will appear as contamination of the white screen by various colors around the edges and possibly near the center, as shown in Plate IV. To avoid these extraneous fields at the time of installation, the entire picture tube assembly can be degaussed. In effect, the 60-cps line voltage is applied as a magnetic field to demagnetize the screen area in the same fashion that the recording head of a tape recorder is demagnetized. Some color receivers use an additional assembly of permanent magnets located around the screen to overcome the effect of local magnetic fields as shown in Figure 15-3. These magnets, generally called *color equalizers,* are rotated to determine the "bucking" direction of the interfering local field and then are screwed closer to the screen to increase the magnetic effect. (Their adjustment will be described towards the end of this chapter.)

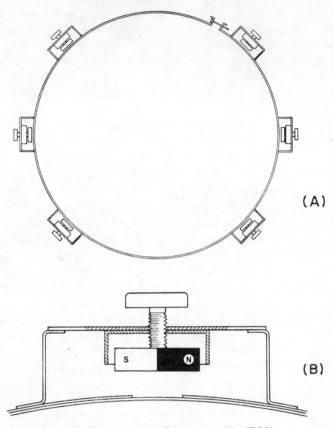

(A)

(B)

Fig. 15-3. The color equalizing assembly. (RCA)

CONVERGENCE

The three electron guns are mechanically aligned and tilted, so that their beams will converge at the hole in the shadow mask and then go on to strike the correct phosphor dot. In addition, a weak magnetic field is applied to each electron beam to provide for any small corrections in convergence. This *magnetic convergence field* consists of two components. One is a constant field, supplied by a PM cylinder located in the magnetic center of a soft iron U, which is located outside the glass envelope (Figure 15-4). The magnetic field passes through the glass into the two iron side plates between which the electron beam must pass. As the PM cylinder is rotated, the magnetic flux varies in strength. A 180° turn reverses flux polarity and therefore "flips" the beam up or down. In

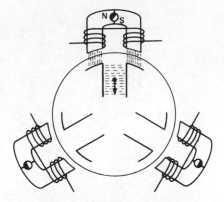

Fig. 15-4. The convergence assembly. (RCA)

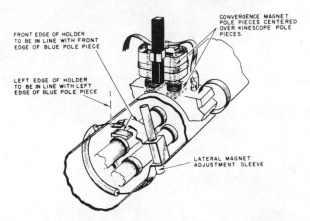

CONVERGENCE MAGNET
POLE PIECES CENTERED
OVER KINESCOPE POLE
PIECES.

FRONT EDGE OF HOLDER
TO BE IN LINE WITH FRONT
EDGE OF BLUE POLE PIECE

LEFT EDGE OF HOLDER
TO BE IN LINE WITH LEFT
EDGE OF BLUE POLE PIECE

LATERAL MAGNET
ADJUSTMENT SLEEVE

Fig. 15-5. Location of the convergence and lateral beam magnets. (RCA)

some sets the convergence magnets are rectangular bars that are moved in or out for adjustment (Figure 15-5). Three equal convergence magnets are spaced 120° apart around the neck of the tube, located over the iron plates encasing each of the three electron beams. These three magnets are set to converge the three electron beams in the center of the screen. In addition, a coil winding is used on each of the three U-shaped pole pieces, as indicated in Figure 15-4. These coils are used to provide convergence at the edges of the screen; their operation is described in the paragraphs below.

To converge the three beams in the center, the three PM convergence magnets are not sufficient because, as shown in Figure 15-6, each moves its respective beam only along a single line and

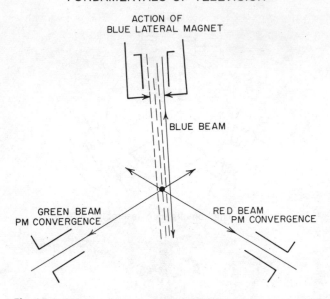

Fig. 15-6. PM convergence and blue lateral adjustment. (RCA)

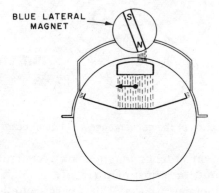

Fig. 15-7. The blue lateral magnet. (RCA)

the three lines may not meet at one point. For this reason, an additional PM convergence magnet is used — the *blue lateral magnet* (Figure 15-7). This magnet controls the sideways movement of the blue beam, as illustrated in Figure 15-7. (Figure 15-5 shows the the relative position of the blue lateral magnet.) Referring back to Figure 15-6, we can see that if one beam, the blue beam, can be moved laterally as well as axially, perfect convergence is possible. (As covered in detail under the alignment portion at the end of this chapter, the blue lateral magnet is adjusted after the three PM convergence adjustments are made.)

Because neither the shadow mask or the color dot screen are spherical, the beams will not converge at the same spot at the center as at the edges. Once the three beams are converged at the center by means of the PM adjustments, this constant correction field must be varied as the electron beams are deflected to the edges. Since deflection occurs both in the vertical and horizontal directions, the correction signal must by synchronized with the deflection signals. This is accomplished by deriving the correction signals directly from the vertical and horizontal sweep signals.

Fig. 15-8. The vertical dynamic convergence signal.

Before describing the actual circuits, the required waveshapes should be considered. When the electron beams are in the center, the dynamic correction signal should be zero. At the top or bottom the signal should be maximum. Figure 15-8 shows a typical dynamic waveform for vertical convergence. The same waveform, at the horizontal sweep frequency, is required to correct convergence at either side, and when the vertical and horizontal signals are added together they will appear as in Figure 15-9. As this signal passes through the coil of a particular convergence magnet, it changes the flux between the iron plates to provide slight corrections to its electron beam.

Fig. 15-9. The combined vertical and horizontal dynamic convergence signal.

CONVERGENCE CIRCUITS

As described above, the convergence of the three electron beams at the center of the screen is determined by the PM adjustment. It is called the *static convergence*. The *dynamic convergence* is controlled by the signals applied across the convergence coils and these signals are obtained from the vertical and horizontal deflection sections. In these sections, a sawtooth waveform is generated that passes through the deflection coils. It is only necessary to change the sawtooth waveform of Figure 15-10A to the shape of Figure 15-10B. This can be done by an approximation of integration and phase shifting.

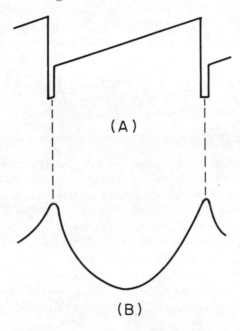

(A)

(B)

Fig. 15-10. The deflection and convergence waveform relationship.

A typical dynamic convergence circuit is shown in Figure 15-11; from it we can see how the waveforms are obtained. Considering first the vertical sweep, we see that a special winding on the vertical output transformer is used in combination with the convergence choke and a resistor, R2, to obtain the vertical convergence signal for the red magnet assembly. By proper selection of the transformer winding and the choke inductance, the RL combination determines the convergence waveshape. The tap on R2 simply controls the amplitude of the curved signal that is fed to the convergence assembly. The return of this signal is through R1, which, at its center setting, corresponds to the grounded tap on the vertical output transformer winding. If R1 is set away from the center, a portion of the sawtooth signal across terminals 1 and 3 is added to the larger curved signal, giving it the appearance of

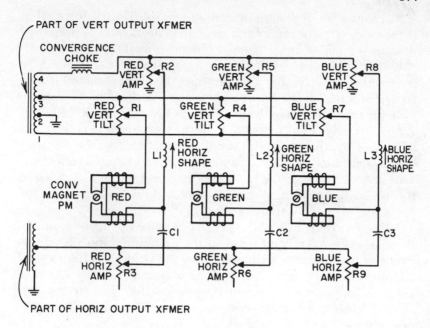

Fig. 15-11. A typical dynamic convergence circuit.

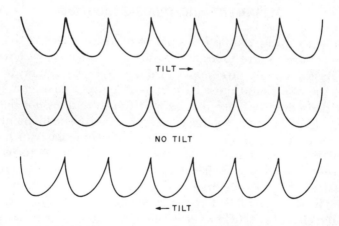

Fig. 15-12. The effect of the vertical tilt control.

being slanted or tilted to one side. Depending which way R1 is set, the tilt will be to either side, as illustrated in Figure 15-12. This has the effect of correcting the convergence of the red beam at either top or bottom.

A separate set of amplitude and tilt controls is used for each of the three electron beams (more adjustment details will be presented towards the end of this chapter). The horizontal convergence signal is added through the coupling capacitors C1, C2, and C3, to their respective convergence assemblies. It is also obtained from a special winding on the horizontal output transformer. The amplitude for each color is individually controlled through R3, R6, and R9 respectively. The combination of the transformer winding, the amplitude controls, and the coupling capacitors with their associated horizontal shaping controls, L1, L2, and L3, determines the waveshape of each of the horizontal convergence signals. Each of the three adjustable coils serves as a phase shifting network for the horizontal signal and thereby controls the waveform.

A closer examination of the circuit of Figure 15-11 will show that there is some interaction between the amplitude and tilt adjustments of each color as well as between the vertical and horizontal adjustments. This must be taken into account during the convergence adjustment procedure and, just like the height and vertical linearity controls, repeated touch-up and a final compromise setting are often required.

ALIGNMENT AND TROUBLESHOOTING

The color picture tube is subject to all of the defects found in monochrome picture tubes and to some peculiar color defects as well. Basically, only three types of defect are possible in the tube itself; the one found most frequently is an open filament. This is easily diagnosed because the neck of the tube does not light up even when the correct voltage is measured across the filament pins. Another defect occurs when the tube has become gassy or has lost some of its vacuum. The symptoms are inability to focus, dim pictures or no picture at all, even when all voltages appear correct. Excessive loading of the high voltage supply is often due to a gassy tube. The third possible defect is internal arcing or shorts between the tube elements. This can be verified by ohmmeter checks. When either of the three above types of defect is found, only complete replacement of the color picture tube is possible.

There are also many defects in the components and circuits serving the picture tube whose symptoms make the tube, itself, appear defective. However, when voltages and resistances are checked, such defects will easily be isolated. Assume, for example, that the screen is yellow instead of white on a monochrome broadcast. We know from the fundamentals of colorimetry and the color diagram that yellow is the result of the red and green electron beams only and that the blue signal must therefore be missing. First we check the d-c voltages on the blue electron gun to see that it produces a stream of electrons. Next we adjust the red and green d-c controls to cut off these two electron guns. Now we should see where the blue electron beam strikes the screen. It may well be that a gross convergence misadjustment causes the blue beam to strike red and green color dots. This means adjustment of the convergence and possibly the blue lateral magnet is needed. In any case, it is always possible to isolate every defect in the color picture tube section to a particular color. Once that is accomplished, it is only a matter of checking d-c voltages and various adjustments to find the defect.

Alignment of the color picture tube can be quite complex if a new tube is installed. In ordinary servicing only a limited amount of adjustment is necessary and even then the detailed manufacturer's instructions should be followed closely. A general guide for all color picture tube adjustments is presented below.

Monochrome Picture Adjustment

The height, vertical linearity, horizontal linearity, width, focus, and brightness must be adjusted for a color tube with somewhat more care than in a monochrome receiver. Nonlinearity can affect the color because the dynamic convergence correction signal may not be able to converge the picture properly. These adjustments

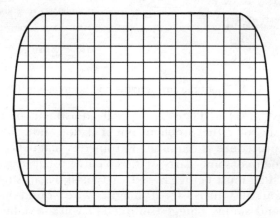

Fig. 15-13. A crosshatch pattern.

are made just as for a monochrome receiver, but to observe linearity of deflection better a special pattern is often used. This can be either a crosshatch pattern, as in Figure 15-13, or a dot pattern. Such a pattern is obtained from a pattern generator connected to the antenna terminals and is very helpful in convergence adjustments as well.

Purity Adjustment

Figure 15-14 indicates where the various components are located on the neck of the color picture tube. From it we see that the purity magnet is located between the blue lateral magnet and the convergence assembly. When slight color impurities exist, such as

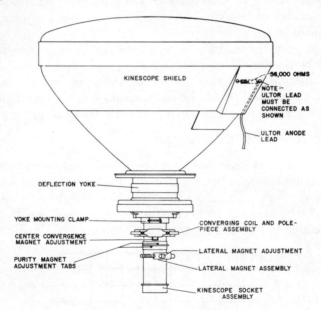

Fig. 15-14. Color tube adjustments and components. (RCA)

the colored areas in Plate V, a small adjustment of the purity magnet may solve the problem, but if it does not, then a more elaborate procedure is required. Extraneous magnetic fields may have magnetized some parts of the picture tube; to remove this effect the tube must be degaussed. A typical degaussing coil consists of about 400 turns of #20 magnet wire wound on a 12-inch diameter and simply plugged into a 117 volt a-c outlet. The degaussing coil is moved around the front of the screen and then gradually withdrawn to a distance of about six feet, at which point the line cord is disconnected.

Before actually adjusting for best purity, the static convergence should be checked by observing the color dots at the center of the screen. A low power microscope simplifies this observation and also shows the results of adjusting the three d-c convergence magnets. Once the convergence is approximately correct at the center, the blue and green guns are cut-off by turning the screen controls down. Red screen purity is obtained by sliding the yoke towards the convergence assembly and setting the purity magnet for the largest possible pure red field in the center of the screen. Then the yoke is moved towards the screen until the red field is uniform over the largest possible area. A number of touch-ups of the purity magnet and yoke position may be necessary.

Older sets have color correction magnets located around the edge of the screen that permit adjustment for impurities at particular spots around the edge. The magnet nearest to the area of contamination, where the red is not a pure red, is turned both according to polarity and proximity to the screen. A little practice with this adjustment will make it very easy to remove impurities at the edges.

Once the red purity has been adjusted, the green and blue screen controls are turned on again and approximately adjusted for a neutral grey.

Convergence Adjustment

As mentioned in the previous paragraph, the center convergence adjustment can best be observed with a low-power microscope, but the use of the dot or crosshatch patterns generator is also very helpful. Plate VI shows a monochrome picture with both vertical and horizontal convergence off and illustrates how difficult it is to adjust convergence without a dot or crosshatch generator. First the red and green PM convergence magnets are adjusted until they converge to give yellow dots or lines at the center of the screen. The blue screen control is set to cut off during this adjustment; when it is turned on, the blue PM convergence magnet is adjusted to produce a white dot or line. While observing the color changes of the dots or lines, remember the effect of the blue lateral magnet shown in Figure 15-6. It may be necessary to adjust that magnet slightly to make the blue converge with the yellow to form white.

Once the center is properly converged, the dynamic convergence adjustments are made. Although the exact sequence of steps varies with different receiver models, the vertical dynamic convergence is always adjusted first. This is done by observing the horizontal lines or the dots at the center, top, and bottom. As shown in Plate VII, the different colors will be separated at the top and bottom if the vertical convergence is off. With the blue screen turned down, the red and green are again converged first to produce yellow. Referring to Figure 15-11, first set all tilt controls to a center position and adjust the green and red amplitude to get best convergence. Only if it seems that convergence is possible at the top but not at the bottom, or vice versa, should the tilt controls be used. Once uniform yellow is obtained, the blue screen is turned on again and its beam vertically converged. The horizontal convergence procedure concerns itself with the color dots or vertical lines at the sides of the screen. Again, the red and green beams are converged first to get yellow and then the blue is added. It will be found that interaction between adjustments requires some touch-up and occasional compromise settings.

Black and White Tracking

Black and white tracking is concerned with the adjustment of the d-c controls and the video signals that make up the Y or brightness signal. All of these adjustments are made on monochrome transmissions and will vary slightly with different receiver models. Almost all receivers now contain a service switch that removes all video and, at the same time, disables the vertical sweep so that only a single line appears on the screen. This line is used to adjust the screen controls and the kinescope bias control to produce a dim white line. Misadjustment of the screen controls shows up as a tinted black and white picture, as illustrated in Plate VIII, which has too much red, and Plate IX, in which the blue component is too weak.

Once the screen controls and the bias control are set, the service switch is returned to normal operation and the green and blue drive controls (Figure 15-2) are adjusted for a good monochrome picture. Occasionally, some touch-up of the d-c bias control is required for correct brightness and the green and blue drive controls may then also need slight touch-ups.

With the above adjustments completed, the monochrome alignment is finished and the color picture tube should produce correct

Plate IV. Poor color purity.

Plate V. Localized impurity.

Plate VI. Lack of convergence in a monochrome picture.

Plate VII. Lack of vertical convergence.

Plate VIII. Excessive red screen adjustment.

Plate IX. Weak blue screen adjustment.

Plate X. Color phase off: too purple. (Motorola)

Plate XI. Color phase off: too green. (Motorola)

Plate XII. Correct color adjustment. (Motorola)

monochrome pictures. It is essential that correct monochrome operation is checked, because there is no way of adequately determining which colors are right on color transmissions. Only when a color set produces good "white" can it reproduce the various colors correctly.

REVIEW QUESTIONS

1. What internal elements are common to all three electron guns in a color picture tube?
2. Does the purity magnet affect only one color or all three?
3. Where should the PM adjustment for convergence be checked?
4. What is the purpose of the "blue lateral magnet"?
5. Where should the vertical and horizontal convergence adjustments be checked?
6. How does R1 in Figure 15-11 affect the dynamic convergence?
7. If only purple pictures appear, which electron gun circuits should be suspected?
8. Should the purity adjustment be made with a white screen?
9. Which two components are moved for a purity adjustment?
10. State the order in which the static and dynamic convergence adjustments should be made.

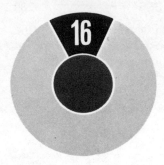

THE COLOR DEMODULATOR AND MATRIX

In Chapter 5 we have shown how the color information is transmitted within the existing 6-mc wide channel by means of the 3.58-mc color subcarrier. We have also briefly described the color diagram and how the color-difference and the Y signals are obtained from the diagram of the three primary colors. In Chapter 15 the color picture-tube circuits were covered, but the color-difference signals were passed over except to state that they are applied at the control grids of the red, green, and blue electron guns, respectively. In the present chapter we will describe the methods and circuits used to remove the color information from the 3.58-mc subcarrier and put it into signals suitable for driving the color picture tube.

A review of Chapter 5 will remind the reader how the three primary color signals are changed into the Y, or brightness signal, which carries all the fine detail, and into the two color, or hue signals, which effectively phase and amplitude modulate the color subcarrier. Figures 5-7 and 5-8 give the frequency spectrum for color transmission and Figure 5-6 illustrates the relationship of the color-difference signals in the form of a vector diagram. We have also indicated that a special synchronizing signal, the 3.58-mc reference, is necessary to remove the phase-modulated color information and have shown in Figure 5-9 how this sync is transmitted. To remove the color information and present it to the picture tube, four distinct steps are necessary. The first step, the generation of the required 3.58-mc reference signals, is quite involved and is covered in Chapter 17, which is devoted entirely to the color sync section. The remaining three steps are the topic of this chapter and are illustrated in the block diagram of Figure 16-1, which shows the basic chrominance section functions. The name *chrominance* is often used to indicate that these circuits deal entirely with color signals.

In the first step, the composite video signal is amplified and the bandwidth is limited to the sidebands of the 3.58-mc color sub-carrier. This is accomplished in the bandpass amplifier. Next, the amplified signal is demodulated by the X and Z demodulators. These stages use the color sync signal as a reference for synchronous detection and produce the X and Z color-difference video signals. By adding and subtracting the correct amplitude and polarities of these two video signals, the three color difference signals, $R-Y$, $G-Y$, and $B-Y$, are obtained in the matrix and amplifier section. The detailed description of the operation of each of these stages will include its mathematical principles and a few typical chrominance circuits. Alignment and troubleshooting information is given at the end of this chapter.

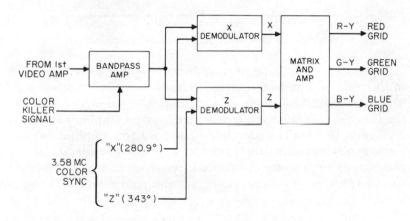

Fig. 16-1. The basic functional elements of the chrominance section.

BANDPASS AMPLIFIER

Experience has shown that very satisfactory color reproduction can be obtained with a hue signal sideband of only 0.5 mc. Earlier color receivers used the so-called I and Q color-difference signals, which provided a 1.2-mc single sideband for the I signal. Having unsymmetrical sidebands required very precise filters and made it difficult to avoid phase distortion on some colors. Now, practically all models use the *X* and *Z* color-difference signals, which have symmetrical 0.5-mc sidebands. For this reason, the frequency response of a typical bandpass amplifier is about 1 mc overall, as illustrated in Figure 16-2. The dip in the center should be kept to less than 15% in order to minimize phase shift of the subcarrier.

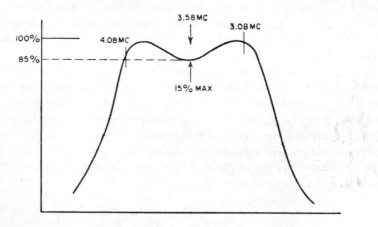

Fig. 16-2. A typical bandpass amplifier response.

Depending on the type of synchronous detectors used, the level of the color subcarrier may have to be in the order of a few volts or as high as 150 volts; this will determine the number of stages in the bandpass amplifier. A typical, single-stage amplifier is shown in Figure 16-3. It is a simple pentode voltage amplifier with a single-tuned circuit in the grid and a tuned transformer in the plate circuit to produce the desired frequency response. The only special features of this amplifier are the connection of a signal

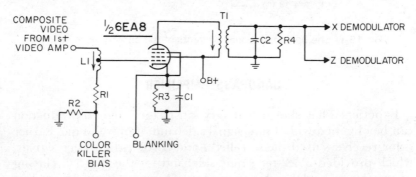

Fig. 16-3. A typical single stage bandpass amplifier.

called *color killer bias* to the control grid and another signal, the *blanking signal,* to the cathode. (The color killer bias circuits are shown in detail in Chapter 17.) The color killer bias circuits prevent any color video from passing through when a monochrome picture is being received. A circuit in the color sync section continuously checks the reception of color sync bursts. When these bursts are missing, as they will be on monochrome transmission, that circuit generates a negative d-c voltage that goes to the grid of the bandpass amplifier and cuts that stage off. Without this color killer bias, the color demodulators could pass some video spikes resulting in colored "noise" on the screen. The blanking signal cuts the amplifier off during the vertical and horizontal blanking period to prevent the demodulation of erroneous colors during the retrace period. This would show up as color bands during the retrace lines.

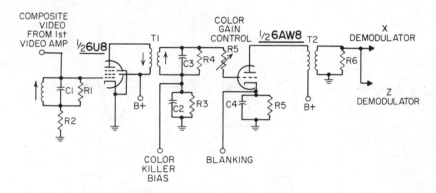

Fig. 16-4. A typical two-stage bandpass amplifier.

In the two-stage bandpass amplifier of Figure 16-4, color killer bias and blanking are again applied and the color gain control is shown. This control is usually a front panel adjustment and, since it affects the amplitude of all colors, it serves to set the degree of saturation. It determines how "pale" or how "suntanned" people will be on the screen. The color gain control corresponds to the contrast control in monochrome sets and only affects the intensity of the various colors, not their hues. Note that in the bandpass amplifier of Figure 16-4, the output transformer is fixed-tuned and has a very broad frequency response. In some receivers, a 4.5-mc rejection trap is included in the bandpass amplifier to keep the intercarrier sound signal away from the screen.

DEMODULATORS

The combination of amplitude and phase modulation is undoubtedly a difficult concept to understand, especially since it is so hard to illustrate in still pictures. Assume that a signal like that shown in Figure 16-5A is the color subcarrier. Note that it varies in amplitude and also slightly in frequency or phase. Now assume that we shall look at this signal only at the fixed, short intervals indicated by the shaded portions of the reference signal (Figure 16-5B).

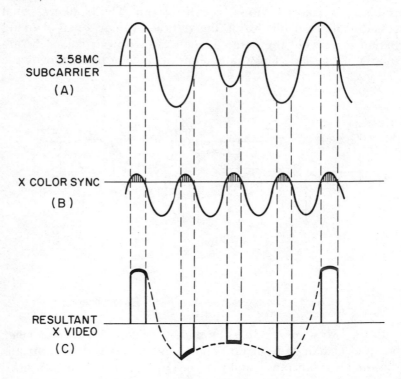

Fig. 16-5. Demodulation of the **X** video signal.

The signal resulting from the combination of the subcarrier, Figure 16-5A, and the *X* color sync, Figure 16-5B, is really only a series of brief pulses, as indicated in Figure 16-5C. When this series of pulses is integrated, or charges up a capacitor, the overall waveform will turn out to be like the dotted line connecting the individual pulses. This resultant waveform is the actual video signal corresponding to the *X* component of the color information. We shall see in later paragraphs how this *X* component is combined with the *Z* component to produce the three color-difference signals.

In Figure 16-6 the same process is used to obtain the *Z* component, but here the color sync signal is displaced by approximately 62° from the *X* color sync phase. Note that the resultant *Z* video signal is completely different from the *X*, although the color subcarrier itself is exactly the same. This illustrates that a signal which is modulated in both phase and amplitude can be demodulated with the aid of a sync signal and will produce different video signals depending on the phase of the sync signal.

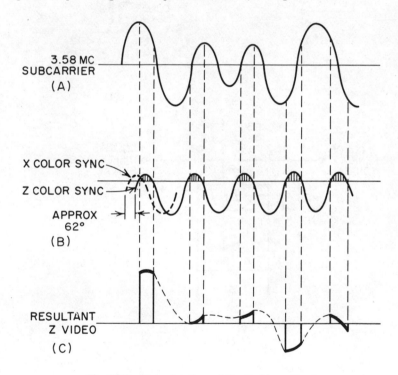

Fig. 16-6. Demodulation of the **Z** video signal.

Different types of circuits can be used to perform the synchronous detection or demodulation. Figure 16-7 shows the three most frequently used demodulator circuits.

Pentode Tube. The circuit in Figure 16-7A uses a pentode tube. The 3.58-mc subcarrier goes to the control grid through the color gain control R1. When the suppressor grid of this tube is less than several volts positive no signal appears at the plate. The tube can

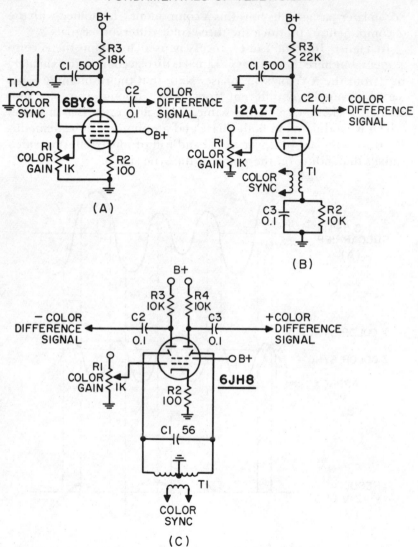

Fig. 16-7. Demodulators using pentode (A), triode (B), and gated beam tubes (C).

amplify only when the positive peaks of the color sync signal are applied to the suppressor grid. While the signal at the plate of the tube consists only of the short pulses illustrated in Figures 16-5 and 16-6, the effect of RC network C1-R3 smooths these pulses out and produces the desired color-difference signal. This pentode circuit, with minor variations, is used in most RCA receivers and by many other companies that follow the RCA design.

Triode. Earlier RCA models use a triode demodulator like the circuit shown in Figure 16-7B. In this circuit, the color subcarrier is again applied at the grid and the color sync signal is applied in series with the high cathode bias, which cuts the tube off except during the negative peaks of the color sync signal. Integration of the output pulses into the color-difference signal occurs again through the RC network at the plate. The triode demodulator has considerably less gain than the pentode circuit and requires a much larger signal from the color sync section.

Gated Beam. The third type of demodulator uses a gated beam tube (also called sheet beam tube). As illustrated in Figure 16-7C, the color subcarrier is applied to the control grid, as in the previous demodulators. The electron stream from the cathode is deflected back and forth between the two plates by the two gate or deflection elements, as shown. This switching is done by the color sync signal. Because of the center-tapped winding of transformer T1, the color sync signal applied at each of the deflection plates will be of opposite polarity. It may be said that the color sync signal is applied in push-pull fashion so that the electron stream is switched between the two plates at the 3.58-mc sync frequency. The effect of this back-and-forth switching is basically the same as that of the on-off switching provided by the suppressor grid in the pentode. One advantage of this gated beam tube circuit is that, as illustrated, both a positive and negative color-difference signal will be available. Because of the characteristic of the gated beam tube, considerably less integration is required at the output plate but a greater amount of high-frequency signal components will be present. (For the sake of simplicity the integration networks and various filters have been omitted in Figure 16-7C.)

A complete chrominance section using gated beam demodulators is shown in Figure 16-8. In order to drive the demodulators, a high-level subcarrier signal is required. This is obtained by two stages of bandpass amplification. The first amplifier obtains the composite video signal from the detector through L1-C1, a 4.5-mc rejection trap. Plate load L2 is tuned to the 3.58-mc subcarrier. The second bandpass amplifier is controlled by the color killer bias and contains the color gain control as cathode potentiometer. L3 provides 90° phase shift for the color subcarrier, which goes to the $R-Y$ demodulator. For this system, found in recent Zenith

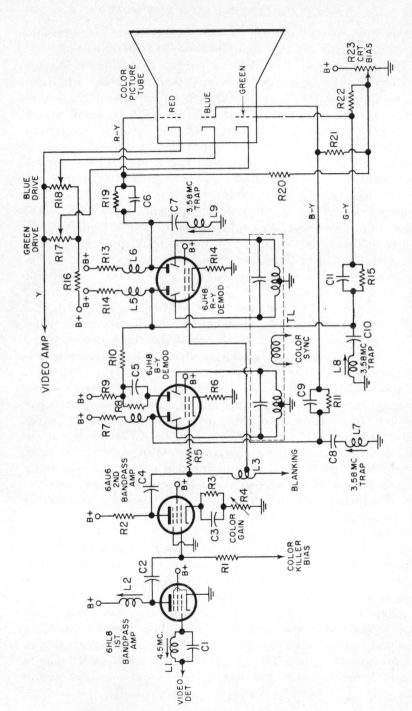

Fig. 16-8. A chrominance section using gated beam demodulators.

models, the red and blue color-difference signals are demodulated directly. Because the signals at the output plates of the gated beam demodulators have an amplitude of several hundred volts peak, they can be matrixed directly and supplied to the color picture tube. Note that each of the plates contains an RC network such as R8-C5 for integration and d-c level restoration. Each of the three color-difference leads, $R-Y$, $B-Y$, and $G-Y$, contains a 3.58-mc trap to remove the components of the color subcarrier and the color sync signal. L4, L5, and L6 are video peaking coils used to improve the frequency response of the three color-difference signals. The vertical and horizontal blanking signal is applied through L3 to the control grids of both demodulators and cuts both tubes off completely during the retrace period. We shall refer again to Figure 16-8 and its matrixing circuits after the principles of matrixing have been explained.

MATRIXING

Matrixing involves restoration of the three color-difference signals from the demodulated X and Z, or, in the case of some circuits, from the $R-Y$ and $B-Y$ video signals. Two important principles are employed here which the reader should know in order to understand the different circuits. The first of these involves the original color signal itself and how it is transmitted. We explained in Chapter 5 that the brightness component is transmitted as the regular monochrome signal, labelled the Y signal. The hues are transmitted by phase and amplitude modulation of the color subcarrier, a process generally described in terms of vector analysis.

Vector Analysis. The rules of vectors are based on the fact that each vector has both magnitude (length) and direction (an angle with the reference axis). All electrical signals can be expressed in terms of vectors that rotate constantly at the signal frequency. At any particular instant they are considered to stand still and may be manipulated with some simple geometry. Figure 16-9 illustrates the manner in which addition and subtraction of two vectors may be performed and the resultant vector obtained. Both the angles and the lengths of the vectors determine the resultant, but if we deal with vectors at right angles we can write the sum easily, as shown in Figure 16-10A. If we can somehow rotate the reference axis, as in Figure 16-10B, vector addition is again quite simple.

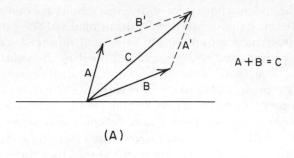

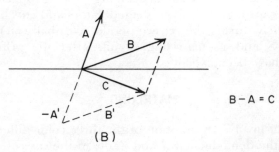

Fig. 16-9. Vector principles: (A) vector addition; (B) vector subtraction.

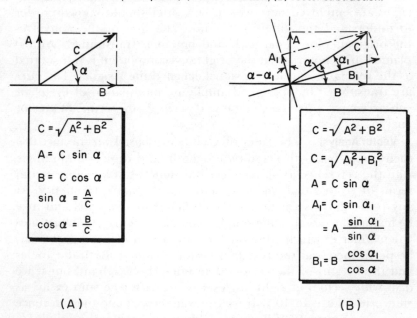

Fig. 16-10. The trigonometry of vectors.

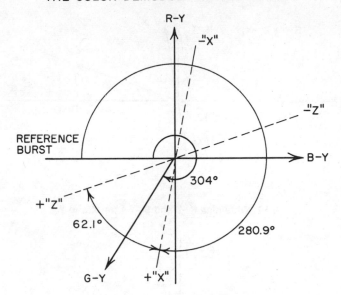

Fig. 16-11. Color difference phases.

The vector diagram of Figure 16-11 shows the phase relationship, regardless of length, of the three color-difference vectors and the X and Z signals. Note that the red and blue color-difference signals are, respectively, 90° and 180° away from the burst reference, while the green difference signal is delayed by 304°. If we now consider the fact that in vector algebra any two vectors can be used to construct any third vector, we can see that by using X and Z, any other vector, such as $R-Y, B-Y,$ or $G-Y,$ can be constructed. As an example, we show two arbitrary lengths of X and Z in Figure 16-12 that have been converted into their corresponding $R-Y$ and $B-Y$ vectors. Note that different polarities and amplitudes of X and Z are added to produce the positive $R-Y$ and the positive $B-Y.$ The same vector construction can be used to obtain any of the color-difference signals. Once the phase relationships or the vector angles are known, only the magnitudes of the signals are important.

In the color demodulator, the phases of the X and Z signals are accounted for by the phase relationship of the color sync signals with the subcarrier. In the matrix circuit, only amplitudes, corresponding to the vector lengths, are necessary, provided that the trigonometric relationships are observed. We have illustrated in Figure 16-10 how the reference axis can be rotated and how every

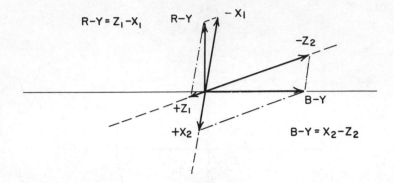

Fig. 16-12. Obtaining **R—Y** and **B—Y** from **X** and **Z**.

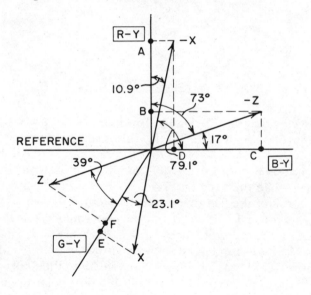

A: $R-Y = -X \cos 10.9°$, $\cos 10.9° = \underline{0.982}$

B: $R-Y = -Z \cos 73°$, $\cos 73° = \underline{0.292}$

C: $B-Y = -Z \cos 17°$, $\cos 17° = \underline{0.956}$

D: $B-Y = -X \cos 79.1°$, $\cos 79.1° = \underline{0.189}$

E: $G-Y = X \cos 23.1°$, $\cos 23.1° = \underline{0.919}$

F: $G-Y = Z \cos 39°$, $\cos 39° = \underline{0.777}$

Fig. 16-13. Amplitude relations of **X** and **Z** to the color-difference signals.

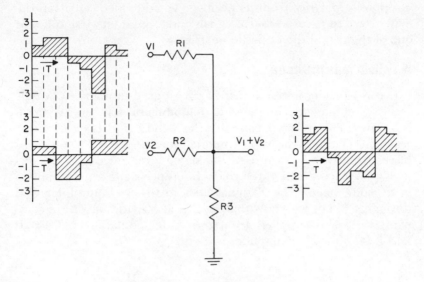

Fig. 16-14. Adding two voltages.

vector can be broken up into rectangular components. We have also illustrated the sine-cosine relationships of lengths in a right triangle. Without delving into basic trigonometry, it is not possible to describe in detail how each color signal is related in amplitude to the X and Z signals, but Figure 16-13 shows the relative magnitudes of the three color-difference signals for fixed values of X and Z.

Signal Addition. The second principle in matrixing is that of signal addition. Figure 16-14 shows two complex voltage waveforms, V1 and V2, applied through two resistors, R1 and R2, across a third resistor R3. It is assumed that R3 is much larger than either R1 or R2. This is a linear adding network and the resultant voltage will be the sum, added simply at each instant of time (i.e., during the first interval, V1 is 1 volt and V2 is ½ volt—the sum will be 1½ volts; during the next interval, V1 is 1½ volts and V2 is still ½ volt—the sum is 2 volts; during the third time interval, V1 is 1½ volts and V2 is 2 volts negative—the sum is ½ volt negative; and so on).

If, instead of adding V2 and V1, we wanted to subtract, the negative of V2 would appear in reversed form and again would be added in the same manner. Subtraction is just addition of a negative quantity. In circuit work we can say that a negative signal is

of opposite polarity from its positive. To add video signals in the
matrix section we use positive signals and to subtract we simply add
one of the two in the opposite polarity.

A Typical Matrix Circuit

Let us consider a typical matrix circuit used in many RCA-type
receivers employing the pentode demodulator. The entire circuit
is shown in Figure.16-15. Note that the X and Z signals are obtained
from the plates of the two demodulators and are fed to different
places from there. Because of the signal levels needed at the picture tube, each of the three color-difference signals are amplified
in a triode stage. The X signal goes to the $R-Y$ amplifier grid
through C6, but we know that $R-Y$ is also made up of a Z component. This is supplied from the Z demodulator via C4 and
R13-R14 to the $R-Y$ amplifier cathode.

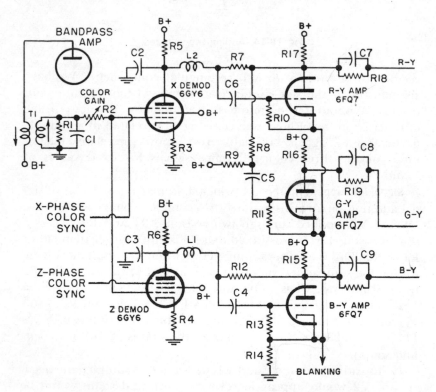

Fig. 16-15. The pentode demodulator and its matrix section.

A signal injected at the cathode appears at the plate at the same polarity, but one injected at the grid is of opposite polarity at the plate. We have illustrated in Figure 16-12 that the $R-Y$ is made up of a positive Z and a negative X and we find that this is indeed so.

The $G-Y$ signal is made up of a much smaller portion of the X at its grid. Actually, we find that the signal supplied to the grid contains X as well as $R-Y$ components from the plate of the $R-Y$ amplifier. This is required because the cathode of the $G-Y$ amplifier is connected to the cathodes of the other two stages and they all receive the same Z signal. This common connection is for circuit simplicity because it permits the blanking signal to cut off all three tubes simultaneously. Because of the common cathode resistor R14, the $B-Y$ amplifier automatically also contains both Z and X components. To reduce the Z component effect here, resistor R12 goes to the plate to cancel out some of the in-phase Z component. The actual mathematical explanation for the various resistance values of the circuit of Figure 16-15 is quite complex, but for troubleshooting and repair work only the correct replacement and not its design justification need be known.

A somewhat simpler matrix network is possible in the gated beam demodulator used by Zenith and shown in Figure 16-8. Here, the demodulators detect the $R-Y$ and $B-Y$ signals directly and, because of the split anode construction, provide signals of equal amplitude but opposite polarity. The $G-Y$ is matrixed by adding the negative $R-Y$ and the negative $B-Y$ with R8, R9, and R10 forming the attenuation of the $B-Y$.

In this Zenith chrominance circuit the three control grids of the color picture tube are returned to the picture-tube bias control, which is also the overall brightness adjustment, but in other circuits, such as Figure 16-15, the control grids are d-c coupled to the plates of the matrix amplifiers. D-C coupling is a requirement we have already discussed in Chapter 11 under the heading *D-C Restoration*. In color sets the d-c component of the picture signal is essential not only for correct shading, but for correct colors. For this reason there is usually a parallel RC network in series with each of the signal leads going to the control grids. The resistor helps to reduce the d-c plate voltage going to the picture tube, while the capacitor reduces the effect of that resistor to a-c signals. Another way of looking at it would be to consider the resistor as a path for the d-c component and the capacitor as an a-c short circuit around it.

ADJUSTMENT AND TROUBLESHOOTING

Defects in the chrominance section can be localized easily because their origin can usually be determined just by analyzing their appearance. During monochrome transmission, the only defects apparent in the chrominance section would be loss of color killer bias or loss of the blanking signal. If the latter is the case, colors will appear only on the retrace pattern. If the color killer bias is missing or ineffectual, the monochrome picture will contain random color patterns which change continuously.

Should the bandpass amplifier become defective, only weak color pictures, or none at all, will appear on color broadcasts. Simple voltage and resistance checks will locate defects in the color bandpass amplifier, just as in any tuned amplifier. If one of the two color demodulators is defective, wrong colors will appear. In sets using the X-Z demodulator systems, loss of the X demodulator will appear as pictures lacking yellow, red, and green, because the X vector contributes mostly to those colors. Loss of the Z demodulator will appear as pictures lacking the blue and green and having, therefore, a more reddish tint. Similarly, in sets where the color-difference signals are demodulated directly, loss of the $R-Y$ section will result in predominantly blue pictures, and so on.

Once the color picture has been studied to determine where the defect is likely to be, voltage and resistance measurements will usually reveal the trouble spot. Occasionally the color sync itself is missing or of the wrong phase. This can be checked by trying to adjust the hue control as described in the next chapter. In difficult cases, signal tracing with the oscilloscope combined with a color pattern generator must be used. This instrument generates a test signal resulting in a color bar pattern in the screen. Because the correct color of each bar is known, the loss of a particular component can be easily observed, even when a color transmission is not available. It is also easier to signal trace with the color bar generator signal because the oscilloscope can be synchronized to show a single line as in Figure 16-16. Here, each color bar is represented by a burst of uniform sine wave, phased to result in the corresponding color. By comparing amplitudes and tracing the signals through each stage, the defect can always be found.

Adjustment of the chrominance section is limited to aligning the bandpass amplifier-tuned networks and to tuning the various

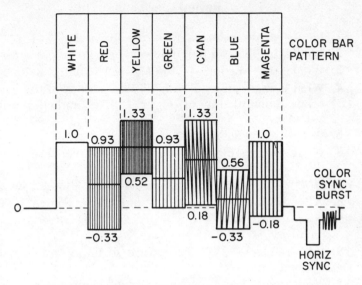

Fig. 16-16. A typical color bar signal for one picture line.

traps at the output of the demodulator. No adjustment of the matrix amplifiers is possible. The bandpass amplifier frequency response can be checked either by using a sweep generator and oscilloscope or by the signal generator and vtvm method, just like the video response of a monochrome receiver. Manufacturer's data as to location and correct frequency setting of the different adjustments in the bandpass amplifier should be followed closely. In general, the overall gain of the bandpass amplifier permits direct connection of the sweep or signal generator to the point at which the video signal is separated from the composite monochrome signal. The color killer bias and the blanking signal must be disabled and, for sweep generator alignment, a special video detector must be connected to the demodulator grid. This video detector is a simple diode followed by a low-pass filter to detect the bandpass response and feed it to the vertical oscilloscope input. Traps tuned to 4.5 mc or 3.58 mc are tuned by using a signal generator and vtvm and setting the trap for minimum vtvm reading. Alignment of the color sync signal phase is described in the next chapter, which deals with the color sync. Chapter 22 covers the detailed alignment of all the color circuits in a typical color receiver.

Review Questions

1. How does the color gain control operate?
2. Why is the phase of the color sync signal so important?
3. What is the function of C1 in Figure 16-7A and B?
4. What is the major difference in the output of the gated beam demodulator of Figure 16-7C and the other circuits?
5. Why is L3 in Figure 16-8 tapped?
6. What should the phase difference between the X and the Z color sync signals be?
7. How can a signal be subtracted from another signal?
8. What is the function of C2 and C3 in Figure 16-15?
9. How would loss of the d-c video level affect a color picture?
10. Why is blanking of the retrace so important in color TV receivers?
11. How would loss of color killer bias appear in monochrome pictures?
12. Where is the most likely defect if pictures appear reddish?

THE COLOR SYNC SECTION

The preceding chapter demonstrated the importance of the color sync signal in demodulating the color subcarrier and we know from Chapter 5 that a short, 8-cycle burst of color reference signal is sent out during the blanking pedestal following each horizontal sync pulse. On monochrome transmission this burst is not transmitted and its absence actuates the color killer circuit. We have shown how the color killer bias is used to shut off the bandpass amplifier and thus prevent any color information from being passed through, unless a color broadcast is received. In this chapter we shall describe the color sync circuits as well as the color killer section, because both operate directly from the sync burst.

Figure 17-1 shows a block diagram of the basic color sync section. The composite video signal passes through the burst gate

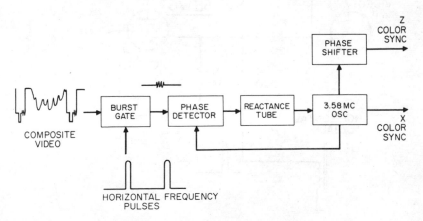

Fig. 17-1. The basic functional elements of the color sync section.

amplifier, which allows only the color sync burst to pass through. This color sync burst is then compared with the locally generated 3.58-mc color sync by means of the phase detector. Depending on the phase difference, an error voltage is applied to the reactance tube, which controls the exact phase and frequency of tne 3.58-mc color sync oscillator. The X and Z color sync signals, or the $R-Y$ and $B-Y$ phases, are then derived from the local oscillator by appropriate phase shifting networks. This overall system is very similar to the horizontal afc described in Chapter 8 and illustrated in the block diagram of Figure 8-1. Only the circuit values and the need for separating the color sync burst are substantially different. Because the color sync frequency is so much higher than the horizontal sweep, and because very exact phase coincidence is essential in the color sync section, its actual circuitry is more elaborate.

COLOR SYNC CIRCUITS

Burst Gate. Starting with the composite video signal, we see in Figure 17-2 how the burst gate actually works. C1 is a small capacitor, favoring the 3.58-mc sync burst, which is coupled to the

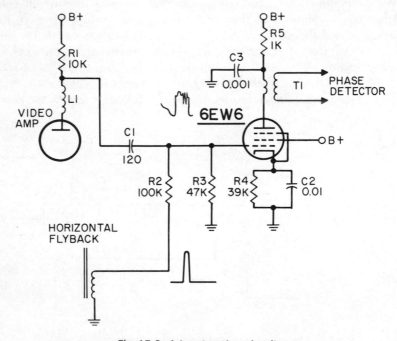

Fig. 17-2. A burst gating circuit.

6EW6 control grid. R4 and C2 provide a very high self-bias that normally almost cuts this tube off. Only when a positive pulse, applied through R2, drives the grid positive enough to overcome the cathode bias, can the signal coming through C1 be amplified. This positive pulse is obtained from a separate winding of the fly-back transformer and will always coincide with the horizontal blanking period as long as the horizontal sweep is properly synchronized. At the plate of the amplifier is a transformer, tuned to 3.58 mc, which presents a large plate impedance at that frequency, resulting in maximum gain at the color sync frequency. In other versions of the burst gate, the video signal is applied to the grid while the positive pulse is used to drive the suppressor, or else a negative pulse is used to drive the cathode. In any event, the horizontal retrace pulse is used to open the gate of an amplifier tuned to the color sync signal.

Phase Detector. The phase detector is a balanced diode detector that essentially is the same as that used in some horizontal afc systems and is also very similar to the familiar FM detectors. Figure 17-3 shows the basic circuit of a typical phase detector. The color sync burst signal is coupled to the center-tapped secondary so that C1 and C2 couple signals of equal amplitude but opposite

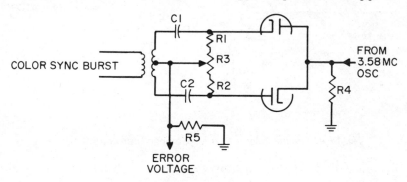

Fig. 17-3. The basic phase detector.

polarity to the two diodes. If the 3.58-mc local oscillator is exactly in phase with these two signals, the two diodes will act as open circuits and no current can flow. This means that the error voltage will be zero when R3 is adjusted to the exact electrical center of the divider R1, R2, and R3. Depending on whether the local oscillator signal is leading or lagging in phase, one or the other diode will conduct, causing current to flow through R4 and R5. The direction of this current, and, therefore, the polarity of the error voltage, depends on which diode conducts or whether the phase is leading or lagging. Thus, any discrepancy in phase between the color sync burst and the locally generated color sync will result in an error voltage. We shall show later that, although this phase comparison action can take place only over 8 cycles, the local oscillator circuit will remain stable until the next color burst is available for comparison.

Reactance Tube. The error voltage, however small, must be capable of changing the oscillator phase correctly. This is accomplished by means of a reactance tube circuit, shown in its basic form in Figure 17-4. We have discussed the properties of this type of circuit in Chapter 8, but a detailed mathematical analysis is not suited for this text. It is sufficient to note that a tube which contains capacitive feedback from plate to grid acts as either a capacitive or inductive reactance, controlled by the d-c bias on the grid.

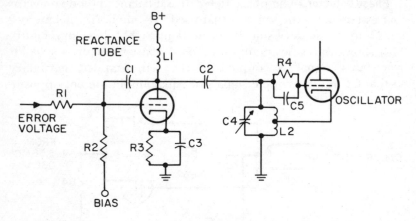

Fig. 17-4. The basic form of the reactançe tube control circuit.

In Figure 17-4 C1 provides the capacitive feedback, but two grid bias sources are provided. The fixed bias is adjusted to give the proper reactance when the error voltage, which can be positive or negative, either adds or subtracts from the grid bias. This is necessary because only a small change in negative grid bias is required to change the reactance of the entire tube circuit. R3 and C3 provide a small self-bias to stabilize the action of this tube. L1 is a choke coil, isolating the tube reactance from the power supply. Capacitor C2 is in series with the reactance tube capacitance and reduces its shunting effect on the tank circuit L2-C4, which is the frequency controlling element of the local oscillator. We have shown a simple oscillator, but actual color sync oscillators are more complex.

Crystal Ringing. Although the reactance-tube system described above is found in the majority of all color sets, a few earlier models used a method by which the color sync burst was directly applied to the color sync oscillator. The oscillator was controlled by a crystal tuned exactly to the right frequency. This crystal was then shock excited by the color burst. The gain of the oscillator tube would then continue the oscillations with reduced amplitude until the next color burst time. This system was found to be less reliable than the reactance tube method, which invariably has replaced it. Because a crystal oscillator operates at a very stable frequency, many color sets now include a crystal resonant at the 3.58-mc color sync frequency as the frequency controlling element, with the reactance tube providing only a shunt tuning effect, sufficient to control the phase of the oscillator.

Oscillator. A complete oscillator and reactance tube circuit, including the phase detector, is shown in Figure 17-5. Although this particular circuit is taken from the 1962 RCA models, it is typical of most other recent color set models. The oscillator contains a tuned plate transformer that is followed by a small LC network which provides the phase shift between the X and Z color sync phase. If we neglect the plate circuit of the oscillator, we see that the screen, having a large resistance in series with the B+, actually serves as the plate in the oscillator circuit because there is a 180° phase shift between the screen and the control grid. This phase shift is due to the pi-network consisting of C16, the crystal, and the reactance due to the parallel combination of L1−C14 and the reactance tube capacity. The frequency-controlling element is really the crystal with L1−C14 contributing a small effect and the reactance tube acting as fine tuning capacitor. C12 and R13 provide coupling and grid leak bias as in conventional oscillators. The plate circuit and T2 act mostly as power driver for the color sync signal and do not determine the oscillator frequency. Tuning T2 does affect the phase of the X and Z color sync signals.

Typical Color AFC

The reactance tube section of the 6GH8 in Figure 17-5 is similar to the basic reactance tube of Figure 17-4 except that the steady-state bias is provided through R12 to the cathode. C10 is the feedback capacitor, which provides the phase shift between plate and

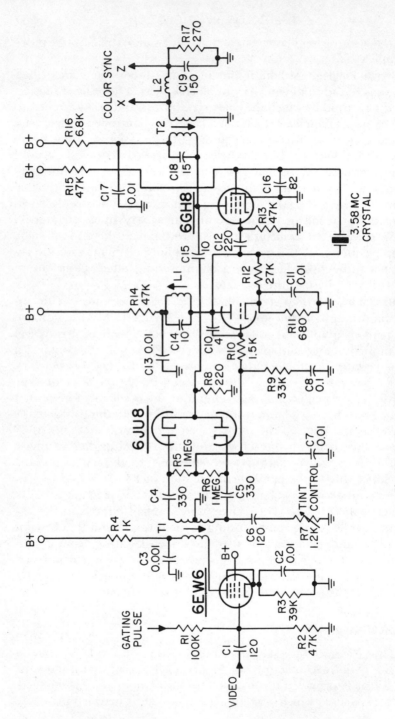

Fig. 17-5. The color sync section of RCA CTC-12.

grid and therefore causes that triode to appear as a capacitive reactance. The d-c grid return for the reactance tube is through R10,
R5, and R6, and then through the double diode 6JU8 and R8 to
ground. C7 and the combination R9-C8 form a filter which keeps
the error voltage essentially constant between color sync bursts.

The burst gating amplifier and phase detector circuit are very
similar to those discussed in preceding paragraphs, except for the
addition of C6 and R7 to the secondary of T1. C6 is effectively
connected across one half of T1 and will therefore unbalance the
color sync burst phase going to the diodes. This affects the error
voltage and, therefore, the phase of the 3.58-mc oscillator. R7 is in
series with C6 and its setting determines the amount of phase shift
introduced by C6. In other words, varying R7 will vary the phase of
the 3.58-mc color sync oscillator and therefore control the relative
phase of the color sync signals as compared with the transmitter
reference burst. Varying the phase of both X and Z color sync has
the effect of varying the phase angle of the demodulated signal,
which changes the hue or color tint of the reproduced color picture. R7 is usually a secondary control, accessible to the set owner,
but not requiring frequent adjustment.

One of the great improvements of the circuit of Figure 17-5 over
earlier color sync circuits is the fact that only four adjustments are
needed. One is the hue or tint control, set for correct color tones on
color transmissions, and the others are alignment of inductors. The
overall alignment procedure, covered in detail in Chapter 22, requires special test equipment for these last three alignments. It is
also described at the end of this chapter.

COLOR KILLER CIRCUIT

Once the operation of the color sync section is understood, the
color killer circuit will not present much difficulty. This circuit
generates a strong negative bias whenever the color sync burst is
not present. In earlier receivers the presence of a signal at one side
of the color sync phase detector was sensed by a gated amplifier
and the resultant rectified signal was used as d-c killer control bias.
This permitted noise pulses that occurred during the color sync
burst period to reduce the bias, even during monochrome transmission. The latest version of the typical color killer circuit is
shown in Figure 17-6 and duplicates the phase detector used for
color sync. By shifting the feedback signal from the local oscillator
by 90°, a strong negative bias will be developed across R5 whenever

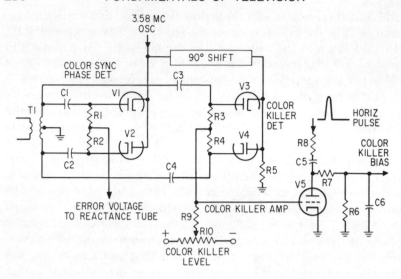

Fig. 17-6. A typical color killer circuit.

a color burst is compared with the local oscillator signal. During the absence of a color sync burst the control grid of V5 is essentially floating. V5 can conduct only during the period of the positive flyback pulse that goes to its plate, but when the grid is negative, current cannot flow through the tube and no d-c voltage develops across C5. When the grid is floating, or essentially at zero voltage, current flows through V5, charging up C5 in such a way that the plate side is negative. R7, R6, and C6 form a filter network that will maintain the negative d-c voltage between horizontal pulses. When noise pulses occur or when the color sync is considerably out of phase with the incoming burst, the correct phase relationship between the signals across R3 and R4 and the 90° shifted oscillator signal will be missing and the high negative voltage needed to cut V5 off will not be developed across R5. This will cause the color killer tube to conduct and will produce the negative control voltage that cuts off the chrominance section.

This scheme prevents a completely out-of-phase color picture from appearing on the screen. Adjustments of this sort are limited to setting the bias level by means of R10, which is connected between a slightly positive and negative voltage. R9 is a high resistance limiting the effect of the setting of R10. Details about the correct setting of the color killer bias level are presented at the end of this chapter and in Chapter 22.

ALIGNMENT AND TROUBLESHOOTING

Defects in the color sync section will be apparent only during color reception. This includes defects that affect the color killer as well, because this latter circuit will produce a killer bias even when no 3.58-mc signal is available from the local oscillator. Defects in the color killer section can be apparent during monochrome pictures if the killer bias is missing or too low. Such a defect is apparent when black-and-white pictures are marred by flashing color streaks. To verify the defect, simply check the killer bias with a vtvm at the point in the bandpass amplifier where it is applied. Then measure the voltage at the plate and grid of the color killer amplifier tube to determine its operation. The most likely defects in that section are due either to a defective amplifier tube, a defective diode, or loss of the horizontal flyback pulse. In difficult cases the oscilloscope is used to trace the flyback pulse and check the presence of 3.58-mc signal and absence of any color burst signal. When the color killer generates a strong negative bias on color signals, this is probably due to either wrong phase of the 3.58-mc signal going to the color killer phase detector or loss of the color sync burst. In either case, the color sync itself will also be wrong, which can be verified by shorting the killer bias to ground and observing the color picture.

Loss of Color Sync. Loss of color sync will, in most recent models, cause the color killer to cut off all chrominance information and result in a monochrome picture. If the killer bias is shorted out by a clip lead or the killer bias level adjustment is set so that colors appear, the picture will be broken up into the primary colors (red, green, and blue) which appear to weave back and forth. As the correct color sync is approached, the picture will momentarily have the correct colors and then change into wrong colors again. If a color bar pattern is used, the effect will be similar to rotating, multicolored barber's poles. This defect, of course, can be due to any of the tubes in the color sync section, but if the tubes operate properly, the defect may be difficult to find. Signal tracing with the oscilloscope is necessary to determine in which stage the defect is. We can check to make sure that the reactance tube and oscillator portions operate by varying the tint or hue control and observing its effect. It should be possible to get correct color sync, at least momentarily, with this adjustment. Oscilloscope checks at the output of the burst gate amplifier will determine if that stage operates correctly. If no defect is found to this point, a complete alignment procedure as

described below will isolate the defect to a particular circuit function and voltage and resistance measurements will then locate the
defective component. The most difficult trouble is an intermittent
or a defect which is apparent only after the set has heated up.
Patience and ingenuity are then called for. One trick often used is
to set up the alignment of the color sync section and then, with all
test leads in place, cover the entire set with a plastic sheet to allow
heat to build up. Blowing hot air from a hair drier on the suspected
circuit is another way to find temperature-caused defects.

Wrong Color Sync. Wrong color sync, locked-in, is apparent when
adjustment of the tint control does not produce correct colors. A
typical illustration of this is shown in Plate XI, in which flesh colors
appear too purple. In Plate X flesh colors are too green. Compare
these two pictures with Plate XII, which shows the correct color
balance and hues. If both X and Z phases are wrong, all of the
color bars will have wrong colors. If only the Z phase is off, then
the red will be correct; if the X phase is wrong, then the blue will
be correct. In either case, the defect must either be in the phase
shift network, T2 in Figure 17-5, or in the demodulator and matrix
section.

Alignment. Alignment instructions will vary between different
models and manufacturers, but the overall procedure consists of
four basic steps. First, the oscillator output transformer (T2 in
Figure 17-5) is peaked for maximum output. This is done by connecting the vtvm through a 500K isolating resistor to one side of
the phase detector (either R5 or R6 in Figure 17-5) and peaking the
transformer for maximum vtmv reading. This is done while the
output to the gating amplifier is grounded by a clip lead. The
second step consists of peaking the phase detector transformer (T1
in Figure 17-5). The short is removed from the gating amplifier
and either a color transmission or the signal from a color bar generator must be available. T1 is tuned for maximum vtvm reading,
but the color sync oscillator must be in sync so that the burst and
the locally generated signal are in phase. If this is not possible,
proceed with the third step and repeat step two later. The third
adjustment tunes the reactance-tube load LC circuit. Now the clip
lead is used to ground the error voltage (the junction of R9 and
R10 in Figure 17-5) and the coil, L1, is adjusted until correct
colors appear. They may not lock-in, but drift through their correct
tints slowly. With the error voltage short removed, L1 is tuned for
correct colors and best lock-in. The hue or tint control is set to

approximately midpoint at this time and a compromise setting of the reactance plate load coil, the tuning of the phase detector transformer, and the tint control is reached. With a color bar generator and the oscilloscope, it is possible to check the range of the tint control by observing the phase shift of the test signal at the $R-Y$ output amplifier.

After the color sync is aligned, the color killer level adjustment (R10 in Figure 17-6) is made on a strong monochrome picture. It is set until all color interference disappears completely. The threshold or level control is reset on a weak color signal to make sure that it does not cut off the chrominance section.

Review Questions

1. How is the color sync burst removed from the composite video signal?
2. What is the function of C2 and R4 in Figure 17-2?
3. What determines the polarity of the error voltage in Figure 17-3?
4. Which component in the circuit of Figure 17-5 determines the reactance tube characteristic?
5. What prevents large changes in error voltage between the 8-cycle burst periods in the circuit of Figure 17-5?
6. How does the tint control R7 control the color sync phase?
7. How will the color killer circuit of Figure 17-6 perform if the 3.58-mc local oscillator is inoperative?
8. How would a defect in the color sync circuits appear on monochrome transmission?
9. How would a defect in the color killer circuit appear in color pictures?
10. List the four basic alignment steps for the color sync section.

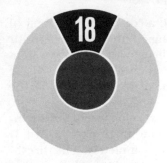

THE AUDIO SECTION

While the picture is the central part of a television set, the accompanying sound is really just as important, even though people often think of audio trouble in TV receivers as only a minor defect. This chapter deals with the audio section in television sets and will demonstrate that, here too, a good understanding of basic circuitry is essential to efficient troubleshooting.

At the studio, the microphone picks up the sound while the television camera views the scene. The electrical signals produced by the microphone are amplified so that they can frequency modulate a separate r-f carrier that is 4.5-mc higher than the video r-f carrier. Frequency modulation means that the center frequency of the r-f signal is varied at the particular audio frequency. In television sound, the maximum frequency change permissible for 100% modulation is 25 kc above and below the carrier. Thus, the only difference between the TV FM carrier and the broadcast FM carrier is the width of the sidebands, which is ±75 kc for broadcast FM and ±25 kc for TV FM. The actual frequencies are somewhat different, too, since the TV FM falls into the respective TV channels, while the broadcast FM band extends from 88 to 108 mc.

At the television receiver, both the video and the audio carrier are amplified by the r-f stages and converted to the i-f. Here, however, the audio i-f carrier is 4.5-mc lower in frequency than the video carrier because only the difference frequencies are amplified. In the i-f section the audio carrier is amplified much less than the video portion, mostly due to the bandpass characteristics of the i-f response curves shown in Figures 12-1 and 12-2. The audio i-f signal is purposely kept below the video portion to avoid interference of the sound with the picture. At the detector the amplitude envelope of the i-f signal produces the video signal.

Another effect of the nonlinear characteristics of the detector diode is that the video and the audio i-f signals produce a beat signal at 4.5 mc which contains the amplitude envelope of the video and the frequency-modulated characteristic of the audio signal. It is this 4.5-mc beat signal that is used as "second i-f" of the audio.

Before describing the actual audio section, mention must be made of an earlier audio system used in TV receivers until about 1954. In this system the audio i-f was taken directly from the i-f section, usually through a trap circuit in the first or second i-f stages, and then fed to the audio section. These early receivers usually operated at an i-f of 21 to 26 mc and the audio i-f was 21.25 mc. Because the second heterodyning in the detector did not take place, the audio i-f signal did not contain the video amplitude modulation, but it was very weak and required several stages of amplification before it could drive the FM detector. The 4.5-mc system, often called the *Intercarrier Sound System,* is used in all present-day models. It has the advantage of being practically insensitive to the fine tuning control at the r-f tuner, and requires fewer amplifier stages.

TV FM CIRCUITS

Every audio section consists of the three basic functions shown in Figure 18-1 *(1, 2,* and *3),* although in some receivers two of these functions are performed in a single stage. The take-off point of the 4.5-mc audio i-f signal may be at the video amplifier or at the video detector, but in all cases a sharply-tuned circuit is used to trap out most of the 4.5-mc signal from the composite video. We refer the reader to Chapter 11 and Figure 11-4 for typical connections of the 4.5-mc take-off resonant circuit.

The three basic functions of the audio section can be visualized if we look at the three signals shown in Figure 18-2. For the sake

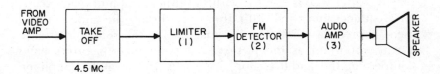

Fig. 18-1. The basic functional elements of the TV audio section.

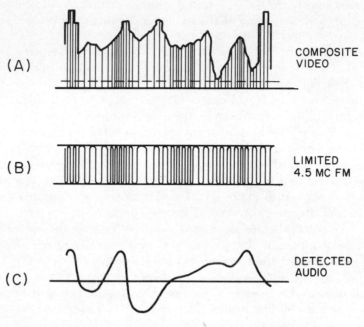

(A) COMPOSITE VIDEO

(B) LIMITED 4.5 MC FM

(C) DETECTED AUDIO

Fig. 18-2. Signals found in TV audio circuits.

of illustration, the actual frequency relations have been somewhat distorted, otherwise the 4.5-mc FM signal could not be seen. In Figure 18-2A, the 4.5-mc signal is shown, amplitude modulated by the video, just as it is removed from the video amplifier. It must be clipped and limited (and usually amplified as well), before the FM detector can demodulate the frequency changes into the audio signal. The limited 4.5-mc signal is shown in Figure 18-2B, and the detected signal is shown in Figure 18-2C. Finally, the audio signal must be amplified sufficiently to drive the loudspeaker. These three functions, limiting, detecting, and audio amplification, are essential and are used in all models, even in those older sets using the separate sound i-f system.

The reader who is familiar with FM tuners will find that, except for frequency and bandwidth, these circuits are the same as those used in broadcast FM sets. Because in TV the sound is usually not as important as the picture, many set manufacturers have skimped in the audio section, especially in the audio amplifier and loudspeaker portions where less emphasis is placed on quality of sound reproduction.

Limiting

The limiter circuit is combined with some amplification of the 4.5-mc signal, but essentially consists of a sharp cut-off pentode stage with grid clipping and plate limiting. The amount of clipping and limiting that is required depends on the type of detector used, since some detectors are less amplitude sensitive than others. In the circuit of Figure 18-3, full limiting and clipping are provided. T1 is the 4.5-mc take-off circuit and is sharply tuned to that frequency. R1 and C1 form a grid-leak bias network that builds up a

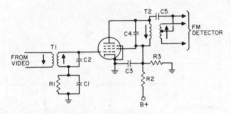

Fig. 18-3. A typical limiter circuit.

negative bias on the grid, effectively clipping off the top of the signal shown in Figure 18-2A. When the grid goes too positive, grid current flows through R1 and C1, setting up a negative grid bias. Limiting of the bottom of the signal occurs in the plate circuit due to the low plate voltage which is held to a fixed level by R2 and R3. C3 acts as bypass to the 4.5-mc signal. This limiting is desirable because in actual practice this smooth base band is lost when the signal passes through the take-off circuit, or else the base level is lost in the video amplifier stage.

The response curve of the limiter in Figure 18-4 shows that after the knee of the curve is reached, increases in input voltage no longer cause increases in the output signal. In some receivers the plate limiting feature is not used, or else resistor R3 is omitted, resulting in less effective limiting, but this depends both on the take-off point of the 4.5-mc signal in the video section and on the type of detector used.

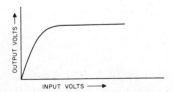

Fig. 18-4. Limiter response.

Detecting

In FM broadcast receivers two types of detector circuits are usually used, the *discriminator* and the *ratio detector*. Both circuits are shown in Figure 18-5, and both use centertapped transformers and double diodes. Their theory of operation and their characteristics are different, although both detect the phase shift between the signals across the transformer secondary and the signal coupled from the primary.

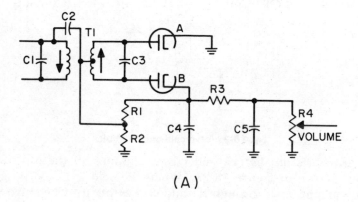

(A)

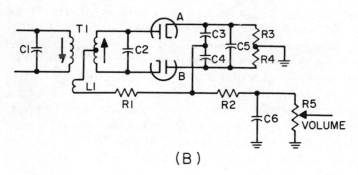

(B)

Fig. 18-5. Balanced FM detector circuits: (A) basic discriminator circuit; (B) basic ratio detector circuit.

FM Discriminator

In the discriminator (Figure 18-5A), the d-c voltages due to diodes A and B will cancel each other across R1-R2 when the signal frequency is exactly 4.5 mc and no signal will appear cross the volume control R4. As the frequency shifts, the signals coupled inductively into the secondary and those coupled through C2 will be out of phase, causing one of the diodes to conduct more depending on whether the phase difference is leading or lagging. This action will produce a signal across R4 because the voltages across R1 and R2 are no longer equal. The detected audio signal is the net voltage across R1-R2, which varies in amplitude as the carrier varies in frequency. C4 serves to filter the 4.5-mc component and the combination of C4, R3, and C5 acts as the de-emphasis network. This latter is simply a low-pass filter, reducing the artificial peaking of the high audio frequencies, which is done at the transmitter in the pre-emphasis circuit.

Ratio Detector

The ratio-detector circuit (Figure 18-5B) also uses two diodes and a centertapped transformer, but here the operating principles are somewhat different. Note that the diode connections are reversed so that a positive signal at the plate of diode A and a negative signal at the cathode of diode B would cause both tubes to conduct. This sets up a voltage across R3 and R4 and also causes current to flow through the secondary of T1 and through its centertap into R2, C6, and R5. Because C5 is a large-value electrolytic capacitor (4 to 10 μfd), variations across R3 and R4 are effectively filtered out. The small inductance, L1, provides a phase-shifted signal from the primary against which the secondary signals are compared through C3 and C4, similar to the phase shifting effect of C2 in the discriminator circuit. Audio signals are developed from the carrier at the junction of R1-R2, but the voltage across C5 is a d-c bias, depending on the average signal amplitude. R2 and C6 form the de-emphasis network here and R5 is the volume control. The ratio detector has the advantage over the discriminator that it is less amplitude sensitive and therefore requires less limiting and clipping.

Both the ratio-detector and the discriminator circuit depend on the transformer for their detecting characteristics. If the centertap in the secondary is not at the exact center, or if the tuning is not exactly on the 4.5-mc center frequency, the response to carrier frequency variations above and below the center will not be the same and distortion of the audio signal will result.

Figure 18-6 shows the response curve of a typical TV FM detector. Note that the linear portion of the curve extends to about

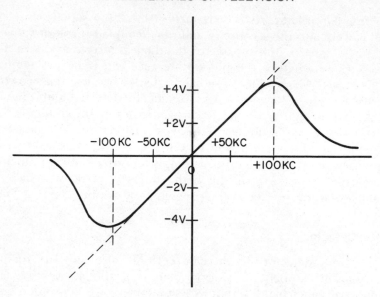

Fig. 18-6. The response curve of a typical TV FM detector.

±75 kc, which is desirable to permit some tolerance in the test equipment used and in the alignment itself. The separation between the positive and negative peaks is about 200 kc, another tolerance factor. While both peaks are of exactly the same amplitude in the illustration, it will be found in actual circuitry that slight variations can be tolerated, as long as the amplitude difference is less than 20% and the linear portion extends to at least 50 kc from the crossover point.

Gated Beam Detector

A third type of FM detector has become very popular in many recent TV models and is based on the gated beam tube. We have already discussed a special type of gated beam tube in Chapter 16; the one used for FM detection is different in that only a single anode is used and the gating element requires less driving voltage. The circuit of Figure 18-7 shows a typical gated beam detector that appears, at first glance, like a normal pentode. Actually, the tube structure is quite different from a pentode. It consists of a cathode, a control grid with a small dynamic range, a screen grid that is really a set of beam-forming plates, another control or gating grid, and the plate. Because of the beam-forming plates, the second control grid receives the plate current 90° out of phase with the first control grid. Therefore, the second control grid is usually called the *quadrature grid*. T1 couples the 4.5-mc signal to the first control grid. A certain amount of limiting is done right at that point because of the cathode bias set up through R1-C1, and because of the construction of the control grid and the beam-forming screen grid plates.

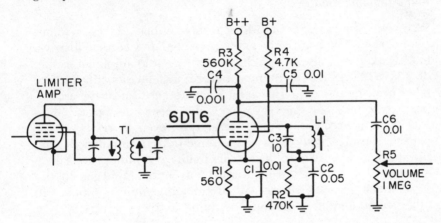

Fig. 18-7. A gated beam FM detector.

L1-C3 is tuned to the exact center frequency of 4.5 mc. This means that, because of the quadrature, 90° phase shift, a high bias will be built up across R2-C2, so that the second control grid effectively cuts the tube off and allows only a minimum plate current to go through to the plate. As the input signal varies above and below the exact 4.5 mc value, the effect of the second control grid will be to allow more plate current to pass. Actually, the gated beam detector operates on the positive portions of the input signal only so that the current through the tube is really a series of short pulses that are integrated at the plate through C4 into the audio signal.

The gated beam detector has several advantages. It provides some grid clipping and is therefore less amplitude sensitive. It produces an audio signal of sufficient amplitude to drive an output tube directly and does not require a carefully-balanced, center-tapped transformer. The only drawback of the gated FM detector is that it requires an input signal of several volts, but this is easily obtained from a single 4.5-mc amplifier stage. The frequency response of the gated FM detector is the same as that of the ratio detector and discriminator, but the quadrature-tuned circuit (L1-C3 in Figure 18-7) provides both the positive and negative peak, which automatically makes the curve symmetrical. The input transformer (T1 in Figure 18-7) merely serves to provide voltage step-up to drive the control grid. It is tuned for maximum and its adjustment is not very critical.

Audio Amplification

Anyone familiar with broadcast radios, public address systems, phonographs, tape recorders, or any other device that drives a loudspeaker, will also be familiar with the audio amplifier section of TV receivers. As mentioned before, in television the picture takes priority and most viewers are not too critical of the accompanying sound. For this reason, few TV sets use elaborate high-fidelity audio sections. The general rule, even in relatively expensive consoles, is to use a single-stage output amplifier driving the speaker. Even where push-pull circuits and multiple speakers are used, the circuits are invariably conventional and hardly deserve much discussion here. All of the audio defects familiar in other sound amplifiers can also be found in TV.

TRANSISTOR AUDIO CIRCUITS

Transistor audio circuits, especially in the audio amplifier, will also be the same as in other transistor equipment. However, because the reader may not be familiar with transistor circuits, a typical complete audio section is shown in Figure 18-8.

Starting at the left, the audio i-f and limiter stage limits the 4.5-mc signal by clipping at the base and limiting through the emitter bias. The base here is back-biased by a small positive voltage, which prevents conduction until the signal amplitude is sufficiently negative to overcome this fixed bias. The ratio detector uses germanium diodes in the same manner as the tube circuit of Figure 18-5B. Note that in both 4.5-mc transformers the primary is tapped to match the relatively high collector impedance to the next stage.

While the volume control in vacuum-tube circuits usually is about 1 megohm, it is only 20,000 ohms in this transistor circuit because of the lower impedance levels throughout. For the same reason, the coupling capacitors usually are in the order of 10 µfd while in vacuum tube circuits audio capacitors usually are 0.1 µfd, at most. In Figure 18-8, a single-stage audio driver is used which

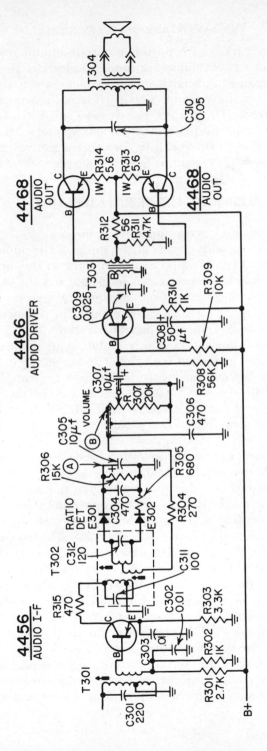

Fig. 18-8. A typical transistor audio section. (Motorola)

also uses some back bias. A push-pull output amplifier drives the loudspeaker in a conventional transistor connection. Bias for the two bases is obtained through a voltage divider going to the center-tap of the driver transformer. This particular circuit is used in a transistor portable TV receiver and drives a small speaker. Push-pull transistor output amplifiers that provide several watts of power usually employ a thermistor, a temperature-sensitive resistor, as part of the base-bias circuit to limit the current when the transistors get hot.

ALIGNMENT AND TROUBLESHOOTING

Audio defects are usually apparent by listening to the speaker or by checking the audio signal at the input to the audio output amplifier. If total loss of audio occurs, any one of the tubes in the audio section can be suspected. In transistor sets the electrolytic capacitors are the most likely trouble source. Of course, if the picture disappears at the same time as the sound, or if both are weak, the defect is not likely to be in the audio section.

To determine quickly in which audio stage the defect has occurred, touch a grounded screwdriver momentarily to the grid, or base, of each stage, starting at the audio output amplifier and going back to the 4.5-mc i-f stage. When a loud click is no longer heard, the defective stage is reached. At this point, normal voltage and resistance measurements should easily locate the defective component.

Distorted sound can be due to a gassy tube, but most frequently it is due either to a misalignment of the 4.5-mc portion or else to a leaky audio-coupling capacitor. Presence of the 4.5-mc signal at the limiter grid can be determined by connecting the vtvm to the grid-leak RC network and tuning the TV set from one station to another. When no signal is received, the bias will be less than about 2 volts. At the FM detector the presence of 4.5-mc signal can be checked with the vtvm at the designated test points. On discriminator detectors this would be the junction of the balancing resistors (R1 and R2 in Figure 18-5A). In ratio detectors it is at either end of the filter capacitor (C5 in Figure 18-5B). When the gated beam system is used, the RC bias network in the second or quadrature grid is usually used as test point.

Alignment of the audio section involves only the peaking of the 4.5-mc pick-off coil or transformer and the alignment of the FM detector. Some sweep generators provide a 4.5-mc beat internally that can be used together with the oscilloscope to align the pick-off coil or transformer by connecting the vertical scope lead to the grid leak bias RC network. With this method, a single resonance with maximum peak at 4.5 mc should be obtained on the scope. To align the FM detector, first move the scope probe to the maximum test point and tune the transformer primary for maximum amplitude. The maximum test point in discriminators is the junction of the balancing resistors (R1 and R2 in Figure 18-5A); in ratio detectors either side of the filter capacitor (C5 in Figure 18-5B) can be used, depending on whether a positive or negative voltage is desired. In gated beam detectors it is usually the RC bias network in the quadrature grid (R2-C2 in Figure 18-7), but other test points such as the control grid or the cathode bias are sometimes suggested by the manufacturer.

After the detector transformer is aligned for maximum, the zero adjustment is made. This tunes the transformer secondary, or the quadrature coil, for the point of crossover, as shown in the curve of Figure 18-6. The test point for this is invariably the point at which the audio signal is taken off.

Alignment of the audio section can also be done satisfactorily with a 4.5-mc generator and a vtvm. The generator is connected to the video detector or the video amplifier and the vtvm goes first to the limiter grid. All 4.5-mc networks are tuned for maximum negative voltage at the limiter grid. Next, the vtvm lead is moved to the maximum test point and the transformer primary is tuned for maximum reading. To zero the FM detector, move the vtvm lead to the zero test point and adjust the transformer secondary for zero, observing that this adjustment makes the meter swing sharply through zero. To check the adjustment, slightly vary the generator frequency above and below the 4.5-mc point and observe that the vtvm goes from zero to maximum, both positive and negative peaks, which should be approximately the same amplitude. Adjustment of the transformer secondary usually affects the tuning of the primary, requiring touch-up. Several touch-ups may be necessary in primary and secondary until the optimum alignment is achieved. In gated beam FM detectors this interaction does not take place, since the input transformer and the quadrature coil are isolated from each other.

An alignment procedure using the TV signal from a station is described in detail in Chapter 22.

Review Questions

1. What is the maximum frequency deviation of the TV sound carrier?

2. What causes amplitude modulation of the 4.5-mc audio i-f signal?

3. Which circuit features cause grid clipping and plate limiting?

4. How does the discriminator transformer differ from the ratio-detector transformer?

5. What is the difference in the diode connection between a discriminator and a ratio-detector circuit?

6. In either discriminator or ratio detector, which part of the transformer is tuned for zero and which for maximum vtvm reading?

7. Which part of a gated beam detector performs the same function as the transformer secondary in a ratio detector?

8. What is the major difference between the capacitors used in the audio sections of transistor and tube TV receivers?

9. What is the function of R1 and C1 in Figure 18-7?

10. What is the function of R2 and R3 in Figure 18-3?

POWER SUPPLIES

In the preceding chapters we have discussed the circuits that produce the television picture in a receiver. In this chapter we shall cover the section that furnishes the power for those circuits. Power-supply defects can affect any or all receiver sections and some defects in these sections can damage the power-supply circuits.

Both vacuum-tube and transistor circuits require well-filtered d-c voltages. Since television receivers generally operate on a-c house current, the major function of any TV power supply will be to convert the 117-volt, 60-cps power from the wall outlet into the required d-c voltages. In vacuum-tube circuits, filament power is also needed, but this can be a-c, though at much lower voltages than the 117 volts. Two main types of power supply are found in TV receivers. One type uses a power transformer and the second type works without such a transformer. In recent models, a hybrid supply is sometimes used in which a small power transformer serves to isolate the chassis from the power line but the rectifying circuits are similar to those of a transformerless supply. For this reason we shall first deal with the latter.

TRANSFORMERLESS POWER SUPPLY

It would seem a simple matter to rectify the 117-volt a-c line voltage and then filter it to obtain a d-c voltage of approximately 110 volts. Although a few earlier sets did use such a system, the deflection circuits and the video amplifier section do not work well with such low B+ voltages. Practically all modern receivers therefore use a voltage doubler rectifier circuit so that the voltage usually is about 250 volts.

Figure 19-1 shows the basic voltage doubler configuration. The 117-volt ac is applied through capacitor C1 across rectifier D1, whicn acts as short circuit during one half of a cycle and as open circuit during the next half. This means that C1 will charge up close to the peak voltage during one half-cycle. During the second half-cycle the voltage at point A starts out at the charged-up value, about 150 volts, and then builds up through D2 to charge up C2.

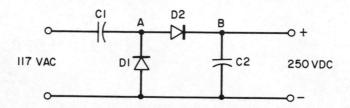

Fig. 19-1. The basic voltage doubler circuit.

Thus, the total charge on C2 would be twice 150 volts, but both D1 and D2 have some resistance and the capacitors have some leakage, reducing the actual voltage on C2 to about 250 volts. This voltage-doubling scheme requires that both C1 and C2 be relatively large so that they remain charged during the half cycles during which the sine-wave voltage goes through zero. In practice, these capacitors are at least 100 μfd, which means they must be physically large and relatively expensive electrolytic capacitors.

A Typical Power-Supply Circuit

A typical, complete transformerless power-supply circuit is shown in Figure 19-2. The voltage-doubling portion consists of C2, D1, D2, and C3, and other important components, such as L1 and L2, help to filter the doubled B+ voltage. In a typical receiver, a number of voltages are required; these are obtained through the resistance network R3-R4, properly filtered by C4, C5, and C6. To protect the power line against short circuits in the TV set, two separate fuses are used here. The #24 fusible wire protects the line against shorts in the series filament string and F1 is a small, replaceable fuse that should open when a B+ short circuit occurs. Without F1, a short in the B+ would burn out D2, ruin C2 and R1, and possibly even damage the two choke coils, L1 and L2. (These two coils are often combined into a single coil, but in the example shown here the manufacturer uses two coils of smaller inductance

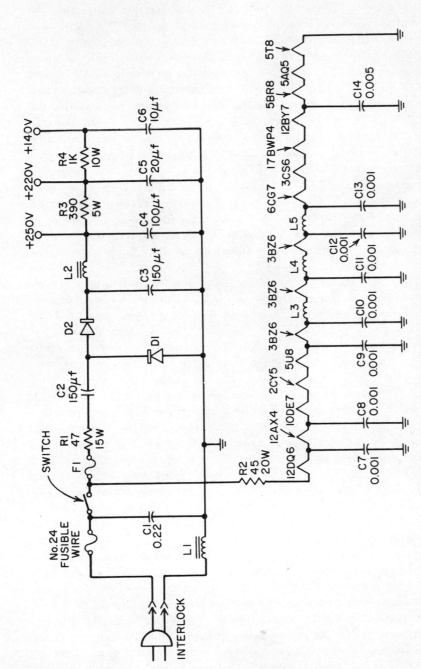

Fig. 19-2. A typical transformerless power supply.

rather than a single one.) R1 is a power resistor, protecting the circuits against sudden line voltage surges.

The filaments of all tubes in this receiver are connected in series, meaning that an open circuit in one tube filament will put the entire receiver out of commission. Note that, according to their type numbers, different tubes require different voltages across their filaments, but all tubes use the same current. This includes the 17BWP4 picture tube and the three 3BZ6 i-f amplifiers. Because of the possibility of pick-up signals on the filaments, decoupling and r-f filtering is provided by coils L3, L4, and L5 and capacitors C7 through C14. Without this decoupling, oscillation in the i-f, the tuner, and the horizontal sweep section might occur. This need for decoupling filaments exists equally in receivers where all filaments are supplied from a single 6.3-volt winding on the power transformer. The series filament resistor, R2, protects the filaments against line voltage surges and also drops the voltage down to the required operating level.

In many receivers the series filament resistor is a special type that has a much higher cold resistance. As the set is turned on, the high resistance limits the current flow to the filaments until the resistor warms up and reaches its final value. Without this resistor, some filaments, which warm up faster than others, draw more current and increase the voltage drop across their slower neighbors. In effect, these slow warm-up series resistors lengthen the life of the filaments. Many tube manufacturers now make tubes with special filaments designed to be connected in series and having a uniform, controlled warm-up time. These measures have overcome the frequent open filaments encountered in earlier series filament receivers.

One of the features of the circuit in Figure 19-2 is the fact that one side of the power line goes to the chassis. If we touch this chassis with a grounded object, such as the human body, it is possible to get a serious electric shock, because, depending on the polarity of the plug in the wall outlet, the chassis may be "hot" with respect to ground. For this reason, all television sets using a "hot" chassis design must provide complete insulation between the chassis and all parts which the set owner can touch. A-C interlocks are standard on all receivers, but on transformerless types they should never be jumped by a "cheater" cord. When servicing a transformerless TV set, an isolation transformer should always be connected between the a-c power outlet and the line cord of the television set. Such isolation transformers are an important prerequisite for anyone attempting to service television sets.

POWER TRANSFORMER CIRCUITS

The classic power supply for most television receivers made before 1955, and for many models made since then, is shown in Figure 19-3. It consists of a power transformer driving a full-wave rectifier tube such as the 5U4, probably the most widely-used single tube-type in home receivers. This tube requires 5 volts for its filament, which also serves as cathode, putting the 5-volt winding on the power transformer at the B+ potential. A pi-filter consisting of L1 and C1-C2 serves to filter the ripple from the B+. Actual voltages vary with different receivers, but output d-c ranges normally between 300 and 500 volts, depending on the ratio of the transformer secondary.

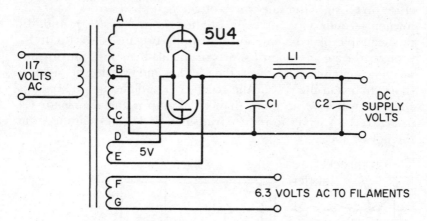

Fig. 19-3. The classic full-wave rectifier supply.

Power resistor networks usually follow the filter to provide the required voltages to the various receiver sections, just as in the circuit of Figure 19-2. The filter capacitors are in the order of 40 to 80 μfd with appropriate voltage ratings. Although Figure 19-3 shows only a single 6.3-volt winding for the filaments, in many receivers several such windings are used to accommodate special filament requirements. The horizontal damping tube in many earlier sets had its filament connected to a special, well-insulated winding because the cathode voltage on that tube was often about 600 volts and heater-to-cathode shorts would occur if the filament were at d-c ground. Recently, tube manufacturers have produced damping tubes with specially insulated filaments that can withstand even higher potentials.

Hybrid Power Supplies

The availability of semiconductor rectifiers, which compete with vacuum tubes in price and voltage rating, has led to their being preferred to the old 5U4, especially since they permit the use of a much cheaper and smaller power transformer. A typical circuit is shown in Figure 19-4 that combines the isolating advantages of the power transformer with the space and heat savings due to the voltage-doubler circuit. A separate winding on the transformer provides 6.3-volts a-c to the filaments of all receiver tubes. Although the voltage-doubler circuit appears a little different from that explained in Figure 19-1, its operation is essentially the same. C2 in Figure 19-4 has the full doubled d-c voltage across it and C1 is charged up through D1. The fact that D1 goes to ground has no effect on C1 since the sine-wave voltage is applied across the transformer secondary, completely isolated from chassis ground. In this example of a recent power supply, two fuses are used: F1 protects the a-c line against shorts of the filament and transformer secondary circuits; F2 protects the rectifier and transformer against short circuits in the rest of the receiver. F1 will be about 3.0 amps while F2 will have no more than a 0.5 amp rating. Capacitor C4 in Figure 19-4 serves to reduce transients and spikes coming from the power line.

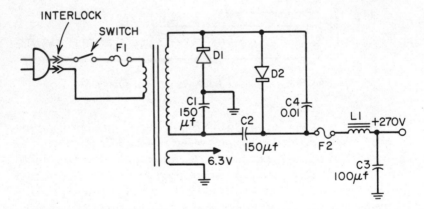

Fig. 19-4. A transformer and voltage doubler circuit.

TRANSISTOR POWER SUPPLIES

Those TV receivers using transistors exclusively are usually intended to operate either from batteries or from the 117-volt power line. In addition, many models use rechargeable batteries,

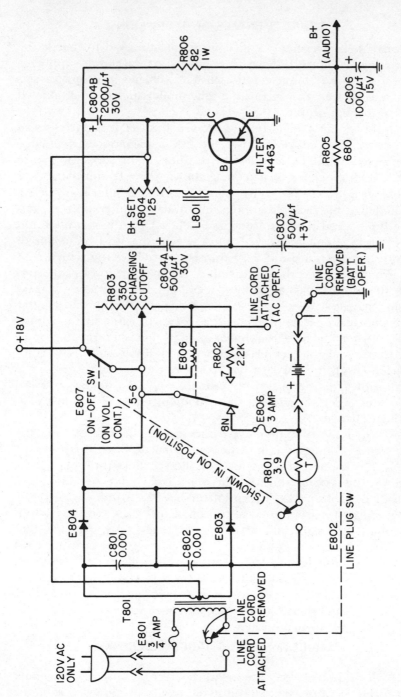

Fig. 19-5. A transistor power supply.

so that the power-line rectified supply is also used to charge the batteries. In Figure 19-5 we have shown a typical power supply for a transistor portable television set. The voltages in transistor sets are much lower than in vacuum-tube models and there is no need for a filament supply.

In the circuit of Figure 19-5 we see a power transformer that steps the line voltage down to the two semiconductor rectifiers, connected in the classic, full-wave rectifier circuit, similar to Figure 19-3. With the power switch on, as shown, the +18 volts dc goes to those sections of the receiver that require little filtering. The remainder of the receiver sections, including the audio portion, gets the B+ filtered through R806 and C806. An additional filter and regulating circuit is inserted into the negative lead by means of L801 and the transistor. This transistor provides the return path to ground and has the negative B+ power return on its collector. Because it must pass all of the B+ current, it will be a power transistor, having a very low resistance between collector and emitter in its normal operation. The base is forward biased by the adjustable resistor R804 and the choke coil L801, but is filtered to ground by C803. A slight back bias is supplied by R805 and this, in combination with the forward bias, controls the current through the transistor. This circuit greatly reduces ripple on the B+ and also provides a certain amount of regulation, especially against line-voltage changes.

A relay is included here to permit charging the battery when the line cord is plugged in and the set is turned off. At that time the battery is connected across one of the rectifiers through a thermistor, R801, and through the relay coil to the potentiometer which is set for charging cut-off. When the battery is properly charged its apparent internal resistance increases and the current through the relay coil and the potentiometer drops so low that the relay opens up and disconnects the battery. When the line cord is removed, the negative side of the battery is grounded, as shown, and its positive side is connected to the +18 volt line through the 3-amp fuse. The filter circuit becomes ineffective and is not needed, since the battery has no a-c ripple and needs no regulation.

ADJUSTMENT AND TROUBLESHOOTING

Power-supply defects are one of the easiest TV receiver troubles to locate because simple voltmeter tests will always isolate the responsible circuit. Each of the suspected components can be checked with an ohmmeter and temporary replacement then verifies the diagnosis. In many cases, the power-supply defect will appear as a total loss of sound and picture. If, for example, the choke coil or one of the rectifiers opens up, there will be no B+ at all. If a filter capacitor opens, excessive ripple will appear as a dark horizontal bar in the picture and may be audible as hum. An open circuit in the charging capacitor in a voltage doubler will result in loss of the B+, but a short circuit in any electrolytic capacitor will often damage other parts as well. In power supplies that have a fuse in the B+, the fuse will be open, a defect that can be seen by visual inspection. Never replace a fuse without first checking the B+ line for a short circuit. If an ohmmeter on a higher resistance scale is connected across the B+, with power off, the meter should first show a very low reading and then charge up. This charge-up effect is due to the filter capacitors.

Occasionally, only part of the receiver appears inoperative because only one of the B+ lines has failed. If R4 in Figure 19-2 were to open up, for example, only those sections receiving the +140 volt line would be inoperative. If C6 should short, however, then the current through R4 and the other series elements might be large enough to blow the fuse F1.

In general, it is safe to assume that most power-supply defects involve tubes, capacitors, semiconductor rectifiers, resistors, and coils, in that order of probability. Short circuits in other parts of the set are often mistaken as power supply defects, but this is easily checked. If the ohmmeter check described above shows a short across the B+ line, the wires going to the last filter capacitor, such as C3 in Figure 19-4, should be disconnected from that place and each one checked for resistance to ground. Then the bus on which the short actually has occurred is easily identified and simple circuit tracing with the ohmmeter will soon locate the guilty component.

Frequently, pictures are reduced in size and brightness because of a low B+ voltage. This is usually due to low a-c line voltage. Since most television receivers do not use specially-regulated supplies, their output voltage will vary as the 60-cps input power varies. Overloaded house circuits can cause the symptoms of low power-supply voltages, but their only remedy is either adequate house wiring or else the use of an adjustable step-up transformer can be recommended. If the line voltage is chronically low, such a transformer can be installed between the a-c outlet and the receiver line cord and adjusted for correct power-supply operation.

If, however, the complaint of low power occurs only at certain hours and the line voltage is at least 110 volts most of the time then a step-up transformer should not be used because it would provide excessively high power supply voltage most of the time, resulting in electrical overload of the receiver and causing various parts to break down frequently.

The power supply usually has no adjustments that can be made by the service technician. A few sets have transformer taps that can be used in case of chronically low or excessively high a-c line voltage and transistor sets have one or two adjustments as shown in Figure 19-5. These should be set strictly in accordance with the manufacturer's instructions.

REVIEW QUESTIONS

1. What is the primary safety item required to service transformerless TV models?
2. Why can we not spot a tube with open filaments by sight or touch in a transformerless TV model?
3. What is the function of C1 in the circuit of Figure 19-4?
4. Why do some receivers use several 6.3-volt filament windings?
5. How is the negative side of the power supply of Figure 19-5 returned to ground?
6. What symptom is indicated by a dark bar across the picture?
7. How does an ohmmeter test check filter capacitors?
8. What is the function of L4 and C11 in the circuit of Figure 19-2?

SPECIAL TV CIRCUITS

While the previous 19 chapters have dealt with the various circuits found in all television receivers, a few circuits and features remain to be discussed which are not part of a particular receiver function or are required only under special circumstances. The first of these circuits is the keyed or pulsed automatic gain control, which is used in practically all modern receivers and which controls the gain of the i-f and r-f amplifiers. Pulses are also used for blanking the retrace lines, as we have seen in color TV. Special blanking circuits are explained in this chapter. In color sets a special delay circuit is used in the video section. This is covered here, too. Remote television control units are an optional feature and, although many different circuits are used in modern TV sets, their common principles are covered in this chapter.

KEYED AGC CIRCUITS

In broadcast receivers as well as in early TV models, automatic volume or gain control is obtained by filtering a portion of the detected audio or video signal and using it as bias to control the gain of the preceding i-f and r-f stages. This has several disadvantages in television. For one, high noise levels will result in the same effect as strong signals and will tend to reduce the receiver gain.

Another effect peculiar to television is so-called *airplane flutter*. When high frequency signals are reflected from a moving object, they are frequency modulated, according to the speed of the moving object. This is called the Doppler Effect and is used in many types of radar and special instruments. Television signals reflected from fast airplanes are frequency modulated at a relatively low frequency, usually below 15 cycles, depending on the channel and airplane speed. This appears as flutter on the screen and can result in loss of vertical and even horizontal sync. The reason for this trouble is that the normal agc control voltage follows the variations due to the reflection and therefore strengthens the appearance of the flutter. Keyed agc operates only on the amplitude of the horizontal blanking and sync pulse and is not affected by the video signal at all. It is less sensitive to noise and to airplane flutter, since it samples the composite signal only during the short duration of the horizontal pulses.

Figure 20-1 shows the basic circuit for keyed agc. We can see that, similar to the color killer stage, the agc tube can amplify only during the horizontal flyback period. The gain of the agc amplifier is determined by the video signal across R3, a portion of the plate load of the video amplifier. R4 is used to control the amplitude of the signal going to the agc tube and sets the agc bias level.

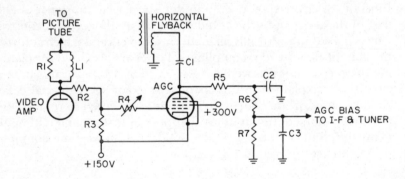

Fig. 20-1. A keyed agc circuit.

This control is usually on the rear of the chassis and is set only at the time of installation. The cathode of the agc tube is connected to B+ to provide a d-c path between grid and cathode. During the flyback period a strong positive pulse is applied to the plate from a special winding on the horizontal flyback transformer. Current flows through R5, R6, and R7, setting up a negative voltage which is filtered by C2 and C3. This bias is then the actual agc voltage. One of the drawbacks of this system is that correct horizontal sync must take place before the agc can work. In the absence of sync, the r-f and i-f gain will be very high, since there will be practically no bias on the controlled stages.

A typical recent version of the keyed agc circuit was shown in Figure 10-5. A unique dual tube is used here to perform the sync separation and the agc function. For both functions the common cathode is at the video amplifier B+ and the signal from the video detector is applied to the common control grid. The agc plate obtains its voltage from the horizontal flyback section, but another video signal, from the video amplifier, is applied to the suppressor grid. Just as for the sync separator, this feature reduces the effect of noise, even when it occurs during the sync time. A common screen completes the circuit. Except for the feature of the double, inverted video signals applied to the control and suppressor grids, the circuit of Figure 10-5 is identical to that of Figure 20-1 as concerns the agc bias generation.

A Transistor Keyed AGC Circuit

A transistor version of the keyed agc circuit of Figure 20-1 is shown in Figure 20-2. This circuit uses two stages to accomplish the same effect. The first transistor contains all the elements of the keyed agc system, but here the control bias is obtained at the emitter, which drives a straight d-c amplifier. In transistor sets, the agc draws considerably more current than in tube sets and therefore the extra stage is necessary.

Keyed agc systems are rarely a source of defects, though the tube itself and the flyback winding can fail. In that case, the symptom

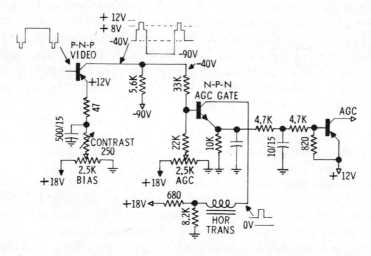

Fig. 20-2. A transistor keyed agc system. (Motorola)

invariably is excessively strong pictures and overloading of the i-f stages. A simple voltmeter check on the agc bias bus will show at once whether bias is developed or not. Voltmeter and ohmmeter checks will then locate the defective component.

RETRACE BLANKING CIRCUITS

Theoretically, the horizontal and vertical blanking pulses go into the blacker-than-black region and will cut the picture tube off during the retrace period. As the effective levels of these pulses depend on the setting of the contrast control as well as the brightness control, it is possible for the viewer to adjust these controls so that the retrace lines are visible. Horizontal retrace lines during the vertical scan are not usually visible because the space between successive lines is too narrow and they occur too close together. The horizontal lines occurring during the vertical retrace period contain both the "paint" and the retrace period of the horizontal sweep and produce a large zig-zag pattern from the bottom to the top of the picture that can be quite annoying.

A simple circuit is used in many recent receivers to blank the picture tube completely during the vertical retrace period and thus eliminate any possibility of this zig-zag pattern appearing. As shown in Figure 20-3, a portion of the vertical output signal is coupled to the control grid of the picture tube. The signal is shaped and attenuated by R1-C1 and R2-C2 so that a large negative pulse appears on the control grid during the retrace period. If C2-R2 have a long time constant, the negative bias could stay on the control grid for much longer than the vertical retrace period and cut off portions of the top and bottom of the picture. In typical circuits these values are chosen to extend the blanking slightly longer than the actual retrace time, to blank out the top and bottom lines that are supposed to be dark.

In some receivers the vertical retrace pulse is obtained from another part of the vertical sweep circuit and in some sets the output of the sync separator is used for blanking. In all blanking circuits, however, defects are readily identified by the appearance of the vertical retrace pattern. If either C1 or C2 in Figure 20-3 would open, the retrace would be visible on top and bottom — blanking would be missing. If C1 were shorted, this would load the output of the vertical deflection circuit and reduce the height drastically. In addition, current would be drawn through R1 and R2, heating them up and also making the grid positive so that an

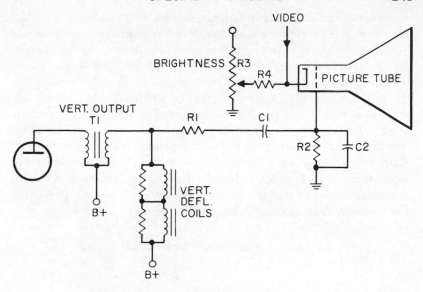

Fig. 20-3. A typical vertical blanking circuit.

excessively bright picture would appear. A short of C2 would ground the control grid and short out the blanking signal, making the retrace pattern visible on the screen. Similar reasoning can be used to determine defects of the remaining circuit components. In all cases, ohmmeter checks and signal tracing with the oscilloscope, as a last resort, will locate the defective component. It should be realized that many viewers may not be aware of the loss of the retrace blanking, because proper setting of the contrast and brightness controls should eliminate the retrace anyway. In color TV receivers, we have seen, special blanking circuits are used to eliminate all retrace patterns automatically.

VIDEO DELAY LINES

We have seen in the previous chapters how the 3.58-mc color subcarrier is amplified and demodulated and the colors are then matrixed until the color-difference signals are combined with the brightness signal at the picture tube. While the color signals pass through a number of stages, each introducing some small delay, the brightness signal usually goes through just one more stage of amplification, the second or third video amplifier. It is not surprising, therefore, that there is a slight time delay between the brightness and the color-difference signals at the picture tube. Because this time delay would result in combining wrong signal phases, a compensating delay is introduced into the brightness signal. For most color TV receivers the delay time is 0.9 microsecond, which is obtained by inserting a small delay line at the grid of the last video amplifier. Earlier sets used actual cables but now a network such as that shown in Figure 20-4 is generally used. The video signal must charge up each capacitor and build up a field in each section of the coils—this process will delay the signal. This combination of capacitors and inductance is the electrical equivalent of the series inductance and shunt capacitance of a transmission line, but the values here are chosen to present a uniform 0.9-microsecond delay to all video frequencies.

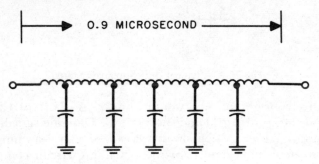

Fig. 20-4. A delay circuit.

In most receivers the delay circuit is a single package. If it becomes defective, it must be replaced by an exact duplicate. Either an open circuit in the coil or a short in a capacitor will be the usual defect that will result in loss of video signal. If only one capacitor opens, the effect is hardly noticeable. In practice, the delay circuit causes trouble in color TV sets only rarely.

REMOTE CONTROL

Operating a television receiver by remote control usually involves at least three separate sections: the remote command transmitter, the receiver, and the section that translates the received commands into action. Depending on the complexity of the particular model, commands can turn a receiver on and off, select channels, adjust volume, contrast, brightness, and so on. We will not cover all types of remote control systems here, but the basic requirements and circuits will be explained sufficiently to enable the reader to follow the manufacturer's data for all adjustment and troubleshooting.

Earlier remote control models used multiwire cables, but practically all recent systems operate in the ultrasonic region, usually between 30 and 50 kc, and use either sound signals or electromagnetic radiation. If sound signals are used, the transmitter is simply a set of resonant reeds or pipes that is struck by a small hammer as the button is depressed. This high-pitched sound is then picked up by a specially-tuned microphone. Electromagnetic transmitters use an oscillator and a transmitting transducer aimed at the receiving transducer and receiver.

The block diagram of the typical remote control receiver shown in Figure 20-5 includes three stages of amplification, followed by a frequency discriminator. In this particular system, a 39-kc tone causes the motor to turn in one direction while a 41-kc tone turns the motor in the opposite direction. This motor is mechanically linked either to the tuner shaft or to the on-off switch and volume control. A solenoid-operated linkage determines which of the two shafts the motor will drive. If either the 41- or the 39-kc tone is received unmodulated, the tuner shaft will be turned, but if either frequency is modulated with a 100-cps signal, the solenoid will transfer power to the on-off switch and volume control shaft. As shown, the discriminator section determines which frequency is received and then operates either one of two relay amplifiers, closing relays which energize the motor. A separate circuit is used to detect modulation and operate a third relay amplifier that controls the relay which, in turn, controls the solenoid.

The circuit of the discriminator and relay amplifiers in Figure 20-6 shows a balanced discriminator, similar to those used in the FM detector portion of the audio section. Depending on which diode conducts, its associated relay amplifier will operate the relay. To filter out noise pulses and the 100-cps modulation, large series resistors, R23 and R26, as well as filter capacitors C21 and C23, are used in each relay amplifier grid. Additional capacity is provided by C20 and C22 to assure that the 100-cps modulation will affect the solenoid portion first. This allows the motor to turn after the solenoid action is complete.

To detect modulation, a small capacitor couples the 39- or 41-kc signal to another amplifier. A diode detector rectifies the 100-cps modulation, which is then filtered, and the resultant d-c voltage operates a relay amplifier that closes the relay and thus controls the solenoid.

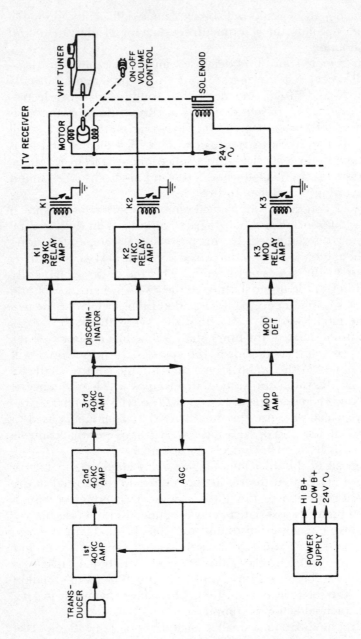

Fig. 20-5. The block diagram of a remote control receiver. (Westinghouse)

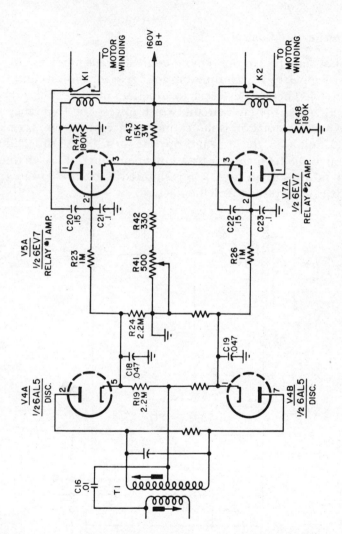

Fig. 20-6. A frequency discriminator and relay driver. (Westinghouse)

A number of mechanical features, such as a gear train that reduces the motor speed, and various cams and switches that stop the tuner briefly at each channel and prevent the potentiometer shaft from turning beyond its stop, make up the mechanical package at the receiver.

Transistor Remote Control

A typical, one-transistor, remote control, transmitter circuit is shown in Figure 20-7, including the four selector buttons and the oscillator coil. The Hartley oscillator operates at 41 kc, unless C33 is shunted across the tank circuit, which lowers the frequency to 39 kc. When resistor R38 is not connected across the emitter bias circuit R37 and C38, the oscillator operates in a 100-cps squelching mode due to the high emitter bias, but when either of the channel control buttons is depressed, R38 is shunted across and lowers the emitter bias to stop the squelching action.

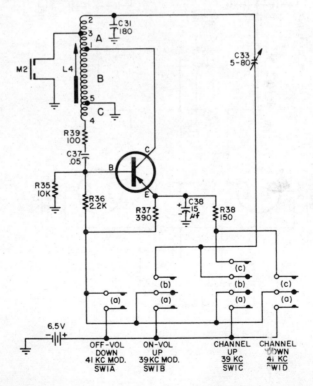

Fig. 20-7. A typical, one-transistor, remote control, transmitter circuit. (Westinghouse)

Figure 20-8 shows all of the components of the remote control system described above. The remote control transmitter with its four pushbuttons is completely self-contained. Next to it is the receiving transducer and two pilot lights, connected to the receiver sub-chassis. In most remote control systems, the receivers contain their own power supply to enable them to operate when the TV set itself is shut off. Since the remote control receiver takes relatively little a-c power, it can be left on for long periods. Some manufacturers offer transistorized remote control receivers that operate on even less a-c power.

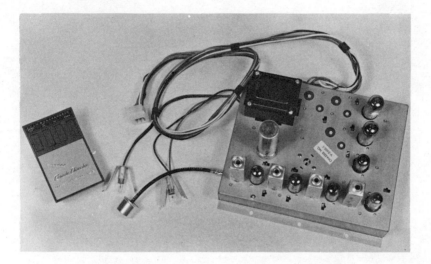

Fig. 20-8. The Westinghouse remote control system.

Troubleshooting and alignment of remote control systems is not really a part of television work, but the technician may be asked to do it. When the remote control system is defective, the section which is at fault must first be isolated. Most frequently, the transmitter battery or one of the amplifiers in the receiver is the culprit. The operation of the system up to the frequency discriminator and modulation detector can be checked by putting the transmitter close to the receiving transducer and checking the output voltages at various stages in the receiver as the transmitter is tuned to one frequency after another. Relay operation can be checked by grounding the right points in the amplifiers to actuate the relays. Poor relay contacts frequently cause intermittent or incorrect operation. Once we know that the system works up to and including the relays, the drive mechanism itself should be suspected. A host of mechanical difficulties, ranging from the simple need for lubrication, to jammed gears and twisted shafts, can occur. Only by closely following the manufacturer's instructions can this type of defect be repaired. In general, it is wise to service remote control systems only when complete manufacturer's data are available.

TV INSTALLATIONS

People buying a TV set like to think that the installation will require nothing more than to plug the a-c line cord into the wall outlet and turn the set on. This often holds true for prime reception areas where all available channels can be received by a built-in or indoor antenna. In fringe areas, and even in many metropolitan locations, the installation takes some special technical knowledge that the average set owner does not have. Whenever an external antenna must be used or connections are made to an antenna distribution system, or where problems of noise, interference, and ghosts are encountered, a qualified technician must make the installation. In this chapter we shall discuss some of the common installation problems and their solutions. Basically, the two types of installation problem that occur most often are weak signals and ghosts; problems with excessive noise and strong interference, although not as common, also contribute to many installation headaches. To acquaint the reader with installations of central antenna systems, antenna rotating, and switching schemes, a short description of each is included in this chapter.

WEAK SIGNALS

All well-aligned TV receivers will give satisfactory pictures with as little as 50 microvolts of vhf signal across the tuner input terminals. Where the signal strength is much less, only an especially sensitive receiver will give good results. Increasing the i-f gain by reducing the agc bias or by peaking the frequency response will not help because weak signals are close to the noise level and both noise and the desired signal will be amplified. In general, receivers using a cascode or neutralized triode as r-f amplifier will have a better noise performance, but if the signal is really weak (less than 10 microvolts), nothing can be done in the receiver.

The best solution for weak signals is to use an antenna system that will produce stronger signals. Here we have several possible systems: antennas with maximum gain at the weak channel; stacking several such antennas; and, possibly, maximum-gain antennas raised as high as practical. Often, a good antenna location requires several hundred feet of transmission line, but the losses on the line would reduce the signal too much. In such cases, a preamplifier or booster should be used as close to the antenna as possible. Such units are commercially available in weatherproof housings and tuned either for a group of channels or for a particular one.

The big problem in cases of weak signals is to determine just how weak the signal is and how a satisfactory increase can most economically be obtained. Companies which specialize in fringe area installations usually have a field strength meter available that is used to measure signal strength on the weak channel, both at the antenna location and at the receiver location. If the signals at both points do not vary by more than about 30%, little can be done with a preamplifier, but a better antenna might help. An increase of 3 db antenna gain doubles the signal. Again, experimentation with different antennas and their locations may be necessary to find the best arrangement.

Remedying Weak Signals

Some helpful hints for getting best reception of weak signals are presented here:
1. The same antenna can pick up more signal if it is higher up.
2. Trees, bushes, and buildings of any sort act as partial attenuators and reflectors for TV signals, therefore the antenna should be as free from obstructions as possible.
3. Do not blindly point the antenna towards the transmitter, but rotate it through 360° for best reception. Sometimes, reflected signals arriving from an unsuspected direction are stronger than the directly radiated signals.
4. Antenna terminals and the transmission line should be free of dirt, oil, grease, etc., to minimize losses.
5. Transmission lines should be kept at least 2 inches away from all grounded surfaces.
6. Compare other nearby antenna installations. Sometimes freak conditions exist that others have already discovered and utilized.

GHOSTS

We have already described the possible reasons for ghosts in Chapter 14. Here we can only add a number of hints, from the experience of other technicians, that may be helpful to the reader:

1. Make sure that the ghosts are not due to reflections on the line by "tuning" it with hand capacity at different points.
2. Explain the causes of ghosts to the set owner so that he can appreciate that this is not a receiver or installation problem but something due to his particular location.
3. Try "tuning" the transmission line by cutting off pieces 1 inch in length for channels 2–13 and ½ inch in length for channels 14–82. This may reduce the ghost sufficiently.
4. Sometimes ghosts are picked up by the transmission line itself and the only solution is to reroute it or else use a shielded cable.
5. Occasionally ghosts picked up by an indoor antenna can cancel those picked up by an external installation. Try to connect both antennas to the receiver and rotate the indoor antenna for best reception. If this works on one channel but results in bad pictures on the others, an antenna switch is a possible solution.
6. Check the manufacturer's data on the directivity pattern of the antenna used and see if one with a narrower beam is available. It may be necessary to use a narrow-beam, narrowband, antenna for the troublesome channel and a different antenna for the remaining channels. A switch would again have to be used.

EXCESSIVE NOISE

Some noise is always present and is received and amplified together with the picture signal. In some locations the noise is so strong that it seriously interferes with the picture. Usually this is locally generated noise and not the normal atmospheric background noise visible on weak pictures.

Noise can be differentiated from other types of interference by its random appearance. Its source is usually an electrical device such as a motor with arcing brushes, the ignition system of an automobile or truck, arc welders, power-line transformers that arc internally, etc. The best remedy is to remove the source of noise. In the case of suspected power-line transformers, the power company will be glad to learn of this trouble because a transformer that has corona or internal arcing means a loss for them. Most other noise sources are not so easily removed. Someone living near a bus stop or garage may only be able to reduce the amount of noise his set picks up.

Noise Reduction

Here are a few suggestions for noise reduction schemes:

1. Try connecting a 10-$\mu\mu$fd capacitor in series with each side of the transmission line at the tuner.
2. Relocate the antenna so that a wall or other shield is between it and the noise source.
3. If twin lead seems to pick up the noise, install coaxial cable or shielded 300-ohm cable.
4. If the noise source is located close to the receiver and cannot be removed, see if the receiver picks it up with the antenna line disconnected. If it does, it might help to ground the chassis with heavy wire or shielding braid to a good ground such as a radiator or water pipe. (See Chapter 19 for the hazards of trans-formerless power-supply models.) As a last resort, use grounded copper screening to line the receiver cabinet and keep the chassis insulated from this ground.

INTERFERENCE

The best solution with interference is to remove the source, but this would often require such drastic steps as dynamiting transmitters or cutting the power to various appliances.

The first step in solving an interference problem is to determine whether it is in the TV receiver itself or due to an external trans-mitter. Poor alignment can cause sound to appear in the picture; arcing in the high voltage section and various defects in the color video portion of a color set can result in interference patterns in the picture. To determine if the trouble is within the set, first try the fine tuning and observe if the interference pattern changes with the audible sound signal. Arcing can usually be heard át the rear of the set and the arc itself is often visible. Color defects can be checked by turning two of the color electron guns off and observing if the interference persists. Microphonics or oscillation in the tuner or i-f section can also be classified as interference and can be identified by shorting the antenna terminals and tracing through the receiver. Poor grounds are difficult to locate, but if tapping of portions of the chassis or of individual tubes makes the interference come and go, it is very likely that a poor ground or a microphonic tube is causing the defect.

External Interference. External interference will usually disappear when the antenna terminals are shorted out. Assuming that it is external, some logical reasoning often helps locate the trouble. If the interfering signal stays locked-in, it is probably due to something occurring at 60-cps intervals. such as X-ray, diathermy, or welding machines. The time of the day and duration of the interference also give a good clue. Amateur transmissions are usually on for only a few minutes, then the transmitter is turned off while the reply is received. A survey of the neighborhood for antennas, industrial installations, etc., often spots the offender quickly. Once the source is located, its frequency can be at least approximately determined from a frequency assignment table, which may be found in most handbooks. The next step is to insert a special filter to reject the interference at the tuner input terminals. Such filters are commercially available and sometimes the filter already available in the tuner input can be aligned to reduce the interference. Finally, a carefully-oriented, narrow-beam, narrowband antenna and shielded transmission line may be needed to avoid picking up the undesired signal. When the interference falls into a TV channel, the only recourse may be a written complaint to the nearest field office of the FCC.

MULTIPLE SETS FROM A SINGLE ANTENNA

One of the basic laws of physics, the conservation of energy, applies to the problem of operating several TV receivers from a single antenna. If that antenna delivers 100 microwatts to one receiver, it cannot be expected to deliver the same amount to two sets. At best it can deliver close to half that power to each of two receivers, but only if perfect impedance matching between the two sets and the antenna is obtained. We have seen in Chapter 14 how important impedance matching is to avoid ghosts and power losses; when two receivers are connected to a single antenna all of these problems crop up again. Not only must the combined impedance of the two receivers not affect the impedance match, but any spurious radiation from the r-f oscillator of one receiver must be kept away from the r-f amplifier of the second set. If both receivers happen to be tuned to two different channels which are 45-mc apart, the oscillator of the set tuned to the lower frequency will be at the same frequency as the r-f amplifier and mixer of the second receiver, causing severe interference. Two different schemes are used for simple multi-set coupling, and both are commercially available in neat little boxes, ready for mounting along the baseboard or on the back of a TV set.

In Figure 21-1A, a resistive divider and impedance matching arrangement is shown which provides some attenuation, but which also gives considerable isolation between receivers. The impedance from any of the three lines is the desired 300 ohms and the attenuation between the antenna and each receiver; between the two receivers themselves it is equal. Other values of resistance and more complex circuits can be chosen to increase the receiver isolation, but the basic circuit of Figure 21-1A meets all of the requirements.

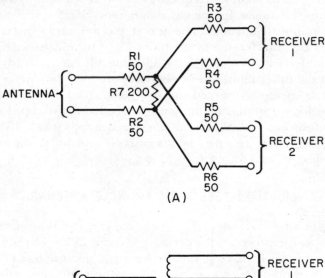

(A)

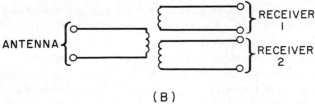

(B)

Fig. 21-1. Two-set coupling.

If less attenuation with some isolation is desired, a transformer coupling scheme as shown in Figure 21-1B can be used. To reduce the coupling between the two receivers, the transformer primary can consist of two sections, each closely coupled to one of the secondaries with maximum isolation between the secondaries.

Most commercially available multi-set couplers use such transformer circuits. For the technician who connects several sets to a single antenna, it is only necessary to determine how many sets must be connected, what the right impedance levels are, and whether the antenna is likely to provide enough power for all sets. Then a suitable commercial antenna coupler can be purchased and installed.

It is difficult to determine antenna output without a field strength meter. Some indication of antenna power can be obtained by observing the agc bias and the picture contrast of a single receiver. If good, strong pictures are obtained with bias voltages of at least 4 volts, the chances are good that two or three receivers can operate from the same antenna. The installation itself consists merely of running the required transmission lines from the coupler to each set. Coupler location should be chosen to result in the shortest lengths of lines to all sets.

SWITCHING ANTENNAS

It often happens in fringe areas that several different antennas are required to receive all of the available channels. Often the transmitters of different stations are in widely separated locations so that separate antennas directed towards each transmitter are a possible solution. It would seem feasible simply to connect all antennas together, but in most such cases this will only result in tremendous ghost and interference patterns. Connecting two antennas in parallel to a single receiver not only causes impedance mismatch, but can also add the poor signals received at one antenna to the good signals received from the second one.

Selector Switches. A simple, two-pole selector switch is the answer in many cases where separate antennas are used to feed a single receiver. A typical situation is shown in Figure 21-2, where three antennas, tuned to different channels and oriented in different directions, are connected to a single receiver. The circuit is simple enough, but a word of caution is in order concerning the switch itself. Impedance matching is still important and the switch must be a type that has little unbalance and capacity to ground. Antenna switches or rotary switches with proper contact spacing can be used, but a commercially available switch box such as the one shown in Figure 21-3 is usually the simplest approach. The commercial unit can be mounted at some convenient spot near the TV receiver. Switch positions are clearly shown by the numerals and the entire assembly is neat as well as inexpensive.

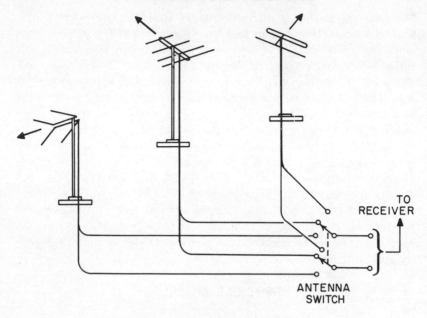

Fig. 21-2. An antenna switching system.

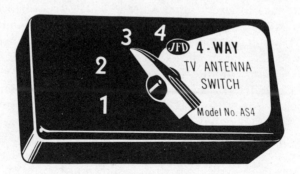

Fig. 21-3. A four-way antenna switch. (JFD Corp.)

ANTENNA ROTATORS

The problem of receiving different channels from different directions can also be solved with a single antenna if the signal strengths are sufficient. It may be necessary to use a high and low band antenna, or else a broadband, directional array, but the antenna orientation is determined by the antenna rotator. This device is nothing more than a geared down motor, mounted on the antenna mast with a smaller antenna mast being rotated and controlled by the control unit at the TV set. As a new station is selected, the antenna rotator control must be varied slowly until the best picture is obtained. After some experimentation the set owner will know what orientation to select for each particular station.

A typical system is shown in Figure 21-4. While the appearance of control units and rotators varies with different manufacturers, the principle of operation remains basically the same. In order to avoid running 110-volt power from the TV receiver up to the antenna, a step-down transformer is universally used and only 24 volts are used to operate the motor. In some systems a simple

Fig. 21-4. An antenna rotating system. (Alliance Mfg. Co.)

three-position switch is used either to disconnect the motor or else turn it right or left. A light indicates when the mast has been rotated against a stop. These stops are necessary because rotation of more than one turn would wrap the antenna transmission line around the mast. Other control units use a selsyn transformer system, similar to the three-wire control systems used on radar-controlled guns, with a mechanical stop at the control unit to prevent more than 360° rotation.

Whatever system is used, the main problems in installing a rotator are mechanical, mostly concerning the stability of the base mast and the balancing of the antenna in the rotator fixture. From the electronic technician's viewpoint, antenna rotators are simple mechanisms that can be serviced by ohmmeter measurements and by an understanding of rotating electrical machinery. Manufacturer's data should be followed closely for both periodic maintenance and troubleshooting.

ANTENNA DISTRIBUTION SYSTEMS

A simple case of operating two receivers from one antenna can extend into a complex system when the many receivers found in a large apartment house or hotel should operate from a central antenna system. The clutter of antennas on apartment house roofs often results in mutual interference as well as a nuisance to insurance companies and landlords. It is therefore not surprising that practically all new apartment buildings and most hotels use central antenna systems. The installation and design of such systems is a separate field in itself, but since many TV receivers operate from such systems, the technician working on a receiver should at least be familiar with the source of the r-f signals.

Depending on local circumstances, the complexity of central antenna systems will vary. A typical apartment house installation is illustrated in Figure 21-5. A separate antenna is usually used for each channel to assure maximum signal with minimum noise and ghosts and this antenna is then followed by an amplifier chain that further boosts the signal. This boost is necessary to provide power for the many outlets and also overcome the losses on the transmission line and in the isolating networks. It is not unusual to amplify signals from 100 microvolts up to 5 or 10 volts before distribution over the cable. In most new installations the transmission line inside the building is not the familiar 300-ohm twin lead which would require isolation from the walls, but rather a coaxial 56- or 75-ohm cable that can even be carried in the existing electrical conduits.

The outputs of all channel amplifiers are added together in the cable so that all channels are available at each outlet. To assure sufficient isolation between receivers, a separate attenuator is included in each outlet. In some installations the attenuator also transforms the 56-ohm unbalanced impedance into a 300-ohm balanced impedance for the standard receiver antenna terminals.

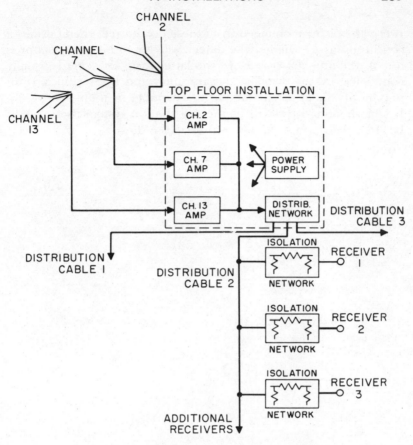

Fig. 21-5. A typical apartment house installation.

Some means must be provided to match the receiver terminals to the wall outlet, even if it is only a connection from one side of the antenna terminal to receiver ground. Although only one line of distribution cable for all apartments in one vertical row has been shown, a number of separate distribution cables, each with a string of outlets, is usually used and the additional attenuation and impedance matching is provided in the distribution network.

For the technician concerned with the operation of a particular receiver on the distribution line only, the quality of the signals obtainable from that line is important. To determine quickly whether the distribution system or the receiver is at fault, many technicians always carry a simple indoor antenna which is connected in place of the distributed TV signal. A comparison between the pictures obtained from these two sources then permits a conclusion as to whether the defect is likely to be in the set or is due to the antenna system. In the latter case, servicing is usually contracted by the installing organization and the technician can only notify them or the landlord of trouble in their system. No troubleshooting or repair of the distribution system itself should be attempted by anyone not authorized to do so.

ALIGNING A TYPICAL COLOR TV SET

Complete alignment of any television set is hardly ever required, but in many phases of troubleshooting certain alignment checks and minor adjustments are necessary. Whenever a major component in a particular receiver section is replaced, that section should be aligned and, in many instances of poor or marginal performance, the guilty receiver portions will have to be realigned. A complete, step-by-step procedure is outlined in this chapter for one specific receiver, the RCA model CTC11. This receiver is in wide use and serves as design basis for the color receivers of a number of other manufacturers who are licensees of RCA. (The CTC11 alignment is substantially the same as that for the later RCA CTC15 and CTC16.)* Although the tuner and i-f response curves of the RCA CTC11 color set are not the same as those found on typical monochrome receivers, the alignment procedure described in this chapter is essentially the same for all TV sets.

NECESSARY ALIGNMENT EQUIPMENT

The most important item of test equipment for any alignment job˙ is the manufacturer's service data. Next, a variety of sweep generators, markers, probes, and oscilloscopes are available, all designed for TV alignment work. The necessary equipments are listed below:

      Oscilloscope: high gain, broad band type.
      Sweep generator: vhf, i-f, and video; 0–10-mc width.
      Sweep generator: uhf (if in uhf reception area).
      Marker generator: covers same points as sweep generator,
         with calibration crystal (can be part of sweep generator).

---

*The complete circuit diagram of the RCA CTC16 is included in the Appendix.

Bias voltage supply: battery with potentiometers or commercial unit.

Dot/crosshatch generator: for color work (can be part of
color bar generator).

Color bar generator: for color work.

Vacuum tube volt meter (VTVM).

Probes: high impedance probe for oscilloscope; detector
probe for oscilloscope; high impedance probe for vtvm;
detector probe for vtvm; high voltage probe for vtvm;
special probes for the generators.

Clip leads: insulated clip leads, assorted.

Special networks, jigs, etc.: as required by manufacturer's
alignment instructions for a particular set.

Before proceeding to the actual alignment of the first receiver
section we should be reasonably sure that the test equipment is
operating properly and that the correct alignment tools are at
hand. Different models require different alignment tools, all of
them available at local electronics distributors. *Never, but never,
should an ordinary screwdriver be used to adjust coil slugs.*

Special care should be taken to avoid using the wrong tool and
thereby damaging the adjustment slug. The time lost in replacing
a complete i-f transformer assembly merely because the tuning
slug was cracked by forcing the wrong tool into it is much greater
than the time taken to get the right tool. The heads of the most
frequently used alignment tools are shown in Figure 22-1. Anyone
expecting to do alignment work on different receivers will do well
to keep a supply of the tools shown at hand.

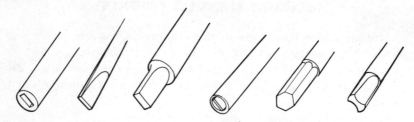

Fig. 22-1. Various alignment tool heads.

ALIGNMENT PREPARATIONS

All of the alignment procedures described in this chapter require that the chassis be removed from the cabinet. This is a very

simple job on some receivers, while in many others the task of removing and then returning the chassis consumes more time than
the actual alignment. A few suggestions are offered here to minimize any difficulties in removing or returning the chassis from and
to the cabinet.

1. Prepare a clear space for the chassis. If the picture tube assembly must also be withdrawn separately, provide a padded space
   for it. Rags or newspaper provide sufficient padding.
2. Study the manufacturer's instructions carefully. Often the
   exact sequence of removing screws and unhinging parts is very
   important. This is especially true in returning the chassis to
   the cabinet.
3. Put all screws, nuts, washers, and other hardware together in a
   safe place. A small jar or plastic bag is very useful.
4. If a transformerless power supply is used in the receiver, be
   sure to connect it to the a-c line through an isolation transformer.
5. Be prepared for a lot of dust and dirt in older sets. A vacuum
   cleaner with a hose and radiator brush is very handy to remove
   this dust.
6. Make sure no transmitters or other radiating equipment is
   turned on in the vicinity during the alignment procedure.
7. Read through the manufacturer's data before starting.

VHF TUNER ALIGNMENT

As a general rule in aligning r-f and i-f stages, the leads from the
generators and those going to the oscilloscope should be shielded
and the unshielded portions should be kept as short as possible.
Other generators or radiating equipment in the vicinity should be
turned off during the alignment to prevent interference. Occasionally, the horizontal sweep interferes with the r-f and i-f alignment
signals. Then the cathode lead to the horizontal output tube should
be opened and a suitable load resistor should be connected from
the B+ to ground to compensate for the loss of the output tube
load. Unplugging the horizontal oscillator serves a similar purpose,
but will upset the B+ balance in the receiver. For the RCA CTC11,
the manufacturer suggests opening the cathode lead, which is a
jumper to ground, and connecting a 2000-ohm, 100-watt resistor
between ground and the +386 volt bus.

Figure 22-2 shows the connections of the bias supply, oscilloscope, sweep generator, marker generator, and vtvm. The vtvm
connection to the mixer grid should only be done when checking

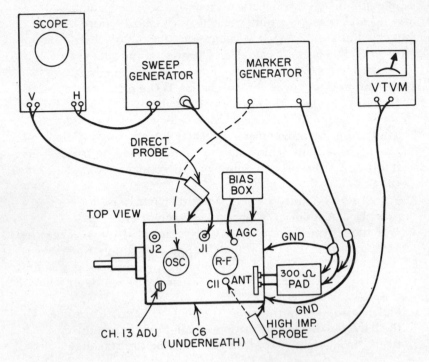

Fig. 22-2. Tuner alignment connections.

the injection voltage. The scope vertical gain should be set for 1 to 2 volts peak to peak and the horizontal scope terminals connected to the sweep generator. Set the scope sweep rate to 60 cps to get a single trace.

Step 1. Tune set to channel 10; set sweep generator to channel 10, markers for 193.25 and 197.75 mc. Adjust the master coils, which are in series with the r-f amplifier plate and mixer grid, for a scope response as close to that shown in Figure 22-3 as possible. Refer to Chapter 13, Figure 13-3 for switch tuner circuit explanation.

Step 2. Change the 2.5-volt bias on the agc terminal to −12 volts. With sweep generator output at maximum, adjust the r-f neutralizing capacitor to minimum scope response amplitude.

Step 3. Return the bias to −2.5 volts and disconnect the sweep generator. If the marker signal generator contains a built-in detector and speaker, or if a separate receiver is available, this step checks the oscillator frequency on channel 13 and on all

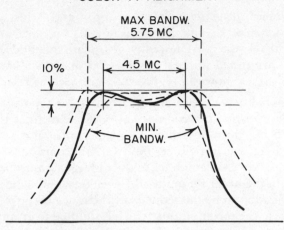

Fig. 22-3. R-F tuner response curves.

lower channels in sequence. The "input" lead from the generator goes to the oscillator tube, where it picks up enough signal to zero beat it with its own internal signal. If the fine tuning control is set at midpoint, the local oscillator should zero beat with the signal generator at 257 mc for channel 13. The series tuning coil for the oscillator is trimmed to produce this zero beat. Another check on oscillator frequency can be made after the i-f has been aligned to make sure that channel 13, and each lower channel, is received with maximum detail and signal strength at the midpoint setting of the fine tuning control.

Step 4. Return the sweep generator connection to the input of the tuner and set it to channel 12. Tune receiver to channel 12 and set marker generator to 205.25 and 200.75 mc. Adjust the input coil of the r-f amplifier for maximum amplitude in the center of the overall r-f response curve.

Step 5. With all settings as in step 4, readjust the coils in the r-f amplifier plate and mixer grid and the coupling coil for best bandpass picture on the oscilloscope.

Step 6. Turn off all generators, connect the vtvm to the mixer grid, and measure the oscillator injection voltage. This should vary from −2 to −5 volts between different channels. If the voltage drops on some channels, the oscillator tube may have to be replaced.

Step 7. Perform oscillator frequency adjustment on channel 6. Repeat step 3, but with frequency of 129 mc and adjustment of the coil in series between channels 7 and 6.

Step 8. Connect all generators as in step 4 and adjust response curve for channel 6. The marker is now set for 83.25 and 87.75 mc and the respective r-f amplifier grid plate coils and the mixer grid coils are tuned for best response as in steps 4 and 5. The response curves shown in Figure 22-3 are used as reference.

This essentially completes alignment of the r-f portion of the tuner. Now only the i-f portion remains. If a uhf tuner is used in tandem with the vhf tuner, then the former must also be aligned. Before aligning the uhf tuner, however, the portion of the vhf tuner which serves as i-f amplifier to the uhf signals must be aligned at the i-f with the tuner set to the uhf position. Again, the −25-volt bias is applied, but now the scope lead is connected through a detector probe to the mixer output, which is shunted to ground with a 330-μμf capacitor, in series with a 180-ohm resistor. Because only one stage is checked here, the sweep generator output will have to be set to maximum and applied to the uhf input jack. A small network, as shown in Figure 22-4, is connected in series with the sweep generator cable to the uhf plug. The sweep generator and marker

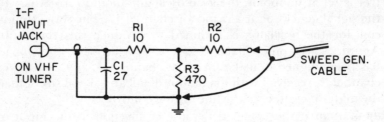

Fig. 22-4. A uhf i-f input network.

generator are set for the i-f, 41 to 46.5 mc, and the mixer input and output coils are adjusted to give an i-f response as close to that shown in Figure 22-5 as possible. Another check can be made as part of the uhf tuner alignment itself by superimposing the i-f sweep signal at the first i-f grid and moving the scope to the video detector output.

UHF TUNER ALIGNMENT

In most areas, only one or two uhf stations are received and a complete tuner alignment is therefore not required; only the respective channel frequencies must be aligned. Two methods can be

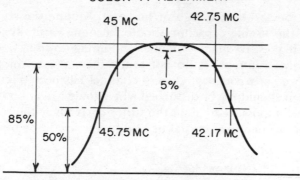

Fig. 22-5. The uhf i-f response curve.

used: (1) The rigorous method of aligning the uhf tuner by itself, which requires a preamplifier for most scopes because there is no amplification of the signal in the tuner. (2) Alignment of the uhf tuner and the i-f section, also, which requires only a uhf sweep generator with a marker generator, or built-in markers, and the oscilloscope.

In either method, the sweep and marker generators are connected to the uhf tuner in the same manner as for the vhf tuner. A −2.5-volt bias is applied to the vhf tuner and the i-f section. The scope is either connected to the video detector through a direct probe, or else to the uhf i-f output point. In the latter case, a detector and preamplifier must be used in series with the scope lead. If the tuner alone is aligned, the bandpass response should be no more than 6 mc between peaks. If the i-f is used too, the regular i-f response curve should appear (as described later in this chapter). In either case, the uhf markers should be checked 4.5 mc apart, corresponding to the video and the sound carrier. For example, on channel 83 the center frequency will be 887.5 mc and this should be within ±10% of the amplitude at either side. The video carrier will be at 885.25 mc; the audio will be at 889.75 mc.

The overall adjustment of a uhf tuner is similar to that of a broadcast radio in that a trimmer tab is used for the high end of the band and the capacitor blades are bent for the low end to track the r-f tuned network with the local oscillator. The oscillator itself is adjusted by using a trimmer at the low end of the band. If only one or two channels are aligned, whether the capacitor plates or trimmer tab are bent for those channels is determined by whether they are at the high or low end. Knifing the segmented rotor of the tuning capacitor should be done carefully, starting with the highest frequency channel and going down in frequency. Be sure that rotor plates do not touch the stator as the tuner is tuned lower in frequency. Once a channel has been aligned, the adjustment should not be disturbed when going to a lower channel. If it seems impossible to align the tuner correctly, either the oscillator tube or the mixer crystal or both may have to be replaced.

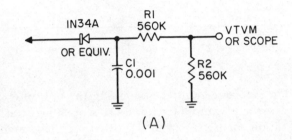

(A)

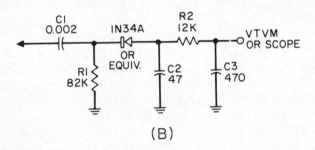

(B)

Fig. 22-6. Detector probe circuits: (A) audio detector probe: (B) video detector probe.

AUDIO ALIGNMENT

Audio alignment can be done with a live signal from a TV station, provided that simple audio and video detectors are available and the gated beam type of FM detector circuit is used in the set, as in our example, the RCA CTC11. The audio and video detector circuits shown in Figure 22-6 can be constructed on a small terminal board or else are commercially available as vtvm or oscilloscope probes. Only the vtvm is needed as test equipment. First the plate of the 4.5-mc amplifier is effectively grounded for ac by connecting a 330-ohm resistor in series with a 2-μfd capacitor from that point to ground, as shown in Figure 22-7. A clip lead is used to ground the quadrature coil in the gated beam FM detector. Connect a −15 volt bias to the tuner agc point to keep the received signal to a suitable level. This may be reduced on weak stations until at least 0.5 volts dc is measured on the vtvm in step 1 below.

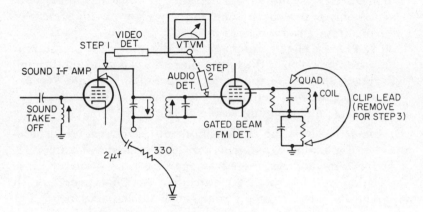

Fig. 22-7. Audio alignment connections.

Step 1. Connect the vtvm through a video detector probe, a capacitive-coupled high frequency detector, to the plate of the sound i-f amplifier or limiter and tune the sound take-off coil for maximum meter reading. This should be approximately 0.5 volts. If agc bias on the tuner cannot reduce it sufficiently, the i-f bias point can be connected to the bias box, too, or else one of the antenna leads can be removed to get a weaker signal.

Step 2. Remove the video detector and the 330-ohm resistor, 2-μfd capacitor network and connect the vtvm through the audio detector to the grid of the FM detector tube. Tune the coupling transformer between the sound i-f amplifier and this point for maximum vtvm reading. To keep this reading to 1.0 volt, the tuner and i-f agc bias voltages may have to be adjusted. Both transformer tuning cores should first be turned outward and then slowly turned toward the center. Retouch each at least once, since some interaction usually exists.

Step 3. Remove the ground clip lead from the quadrature coil and remove the detector probe. Remove any bias from the i-f section and turn the tuner agc bias down to zero volts. Withdraw the core of the quadrature coil up to the top of the coil form and adjust the volume control for normal sound level. Now turn the tuning slug on the quadrature coil slowly down until a peak in sound level is heard. Continue through this peak until a second peak is heard. Reduce the sound level by increasing the bias on the tuner and on the i-f, if necessary, until the sound is distorted. Then carefully readjust the quadrature coil until the sound is clear again. This is repeated until clear sound is obtained only at one sharp point and any slight misadjustment of the quadrature coil causes distortion.

Step 4. Remove all test equipment and disconnect the bias supply. Observe the screen as the fine tuning control is adjusted through its range. Set the fine tuning for maximum 4.5-mc interference in the picture and then adjust the 4.5-mc trap in the video detector stage for minimum visible interference.

In other receivers the audio alignment recommended includes the use of a 4.5-mc signal generator as described in Chapter 18. The above method has the advantage of greater accuracy, since the station signal is more accurate than a 4.5-mc generator. It also requires only a vtvm and some small auxiliary circuits.

I-F ALIGNMENT

When only slight misalignment is suspected or an alignment check is made, the sweep generator-oscilloscope method is usually used. For a complete alignment job, however it is best first to set each transformer, coil, and trap to its assigned frequency. For either alignment, the keyed agc must be disabled; in the RCA set used in this example, the entire i-f agc bus is grounded. Approximately −15 volts of bias is applied to the tuner, which is also set to channel 2 or 3, whichever is not in use in a particular area.

To adjust each tuned stage to its assigned frequency, only a signal generator (such as the marker generator used in conjunction with the sweep generator) and a vtvm with a high impedance probe are required. The signal generator is connected to the mixer grid through a voltage divider, 68 ohms in series and 12 ohms to ground, followed by a .001 μfd capacitor to the mixer grid, depending on the type of signal generator available. The vtvm is connected to the video detector. During alignment it may be necessary to reduce the signal generator output to keep the vtvm reading at approximately 1.5 volts. In the RCA model CTC11 the following steps are required.

Step 1. Set signal generator to 43.8 mc and tune the third i-f transformer for maximum vtvm reading. Two peaks may be possible, but the one with the tuning core nearest to the printed board is the right peak.

Step 2. Set generator to 42.5 mc and tune the second transformer for maximum, as in step 1.

Step 3. Set generator to 45.75 mc and tune the first transformer for maximum as in step 1.

Step 4. Set generator to 44 mc and tune the transformer in the grid circuit of the first i-f stage. Next, tune the mixer plate coil, on the tuner, at the same frequency. The plate coil on the tuner should be peaked with the core near the top of the coil.

Step 5. Set generator to 41.25 mc and tune the third i-f sound trap for minimum vtvm reading. Adjust the sound rejection control for minimum vtvm reading. If necessary, increase the generator output to get a good indication on the meter.

Step 6. Set generator to 47.25 mc and adjust the "adjacent channel sound" traps for minimum meter reading.

To check the alignment approximately, the signal generator can be tuned from 41.25 mc to 47.25 mc while the meter is observed. This should show little variation between 45 and 42.5 mc.

For sweep generator alignment, the connections shown in Figure 22-8 should be used. To avoid interference from the horizontal sweep, the disconnection method described at the beginning of this chapter should be used. All tube shields and the chassis shield

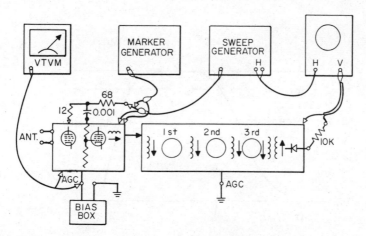

Fig. 22-8. I-F sweep generator alignment connections.

should remain in place during the alignment procedure. Apply —15 volts to the tuner agc terminal and connect another —15 volt bias to the blanking amplifier tube in the color section to keep it from interfering. The sweep generator connection is made to the mixer grid through a pad, as explained in the previous alignment method. To get good frequency markers from an external marker generator, its signals should be loosely coupled to the sweep generator output; the usual method is to clip the "hot" lead of the marker generator to the insulation of the "hot" lead of the sweep generator. If the marking signals appear too strong on the·oscilloscope, reduce the generator output or reduce the coupling by clipping the generator "hot" lead to the sweep generator ground lead.

The oscilloscope is connected through a 10,000-ohm resistor or its own probe to the video detector and the vtvm is used to monitor the tuner agc bias. The bias point for the i-f section itself is again grounded.

Assuming that the stage-by-stage alignment described above has been done correctly, the frequency response curve visible on the oscilloscope should be close to that illustrated in Figure 22-9. With the markers set to each of the alignment points listed in steps 1 through 6 above, adjust each respective transformer and trap for best symmetry and flatness of the response curve. In the RCA CTC11 the third i-f transformer affects the tilt of the response curve, the second plate transformer controls the amplitude at about

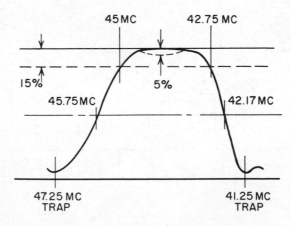

Fig. 22-9. The overall i-f response curve.

42.5 mc, and the first stage controls the 45.5-mc side. By carefully observing the response curve as each tuning core is slowly adjusted, the effect and proper setting for each will become apparent. The trap circuits are set for maximum rejection at the 41.25- and 47.25-mc points.

During the entire alignment, the peak-to-peak amplitude of the response curve on the scope should not exceed 3 volts. During the trap alignment, the scope gain may have to be increased to show the action of the traps. To make sure that the i-f response is a true one, the sweep generator output should be decreased until the scope picture corresponds to about 1 volt peak-to-peak; at this point it should be slowly increased. Neither the tilt, bandwidth, or flatness should change as the sweep output is varied. Excessive generator signal will overload the i-f section and give the appearance of a very flat curve.

After the i-f section is correctly aligned, it may be useful to check the overall r-f–i-f response. For this purpose the same arrangement as described for the tuner alignment, vhf or uhf, can be used. Remember to reduce the tuner agc bias to about −3 volts and connect the sweep generator to the antenna terminals.

HORIZONTAL DEFLECTION ADJUSTMENT

Horizontal deflection adjustment is not usual in monochrome receivers and is used in color sets to determine the efficiency of the horizontal flyback and deflection system. In addition to the oscilloscope, a high voltage probe for the vtvm is required. A milliammeter with a 0–500 ma range and a microammeter with a 0–1500 microamp range are also required. The 0–500 ma meter is connected in series with the horizontal output amplifier cathode, which is accessible through a jumper pin on the chassis. A similar jumper pin makes it possible to connect the 0–1500 microammeter in series with the cathode of the high voltage shunt regulator tube. The following procedure is recommended:

Step 1. Connect the oscilloscope through a low-capacity probe to the junction of the two coils in the horizontal oscillator (a test point in most receivers). Set the horizontal scope sweep to approximately 7.5 kc to get two cycles of the horizontal oscillator signal on the scope. Tune in a good TV channel and adjust the horizontal frequency coil for best locking action when the horizontal hold control is set to midpoint. After good horizontal locking is observed, adjust the "sine-wave" coil in the horizontal oscillator for a balanced sine wave, like the waveform shown in Figure 22-10. Retouch the frequency control coil as required for good lock-in.

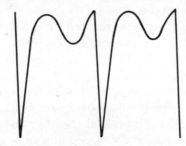

Fig. 22-10. The horizontal oscillator waveform.

Step 2. The plate of the damper tube contains a tuned network called an *efficiency coil,* which acts as filter for the flyback pulses. This coil is tuned for minimum current in the horizontal output amplifier cathode, as measured on the 0–500 ma meter. In the RCA CTC11, the cathode current should be adjustable to less than 200 ma.

Step 3. The grid bias on the high voltage regulator tube is next adjusted by measuring the current on the 0–1500 microammeter and checking the high voltage with the vtvm and a suitable high voltage probe. In the set used as example, the voltage at the picture tube should be 24 kv. With the picture tube set for the least suitable brightness, on a grey picture, the current should not be less than 850 microamperes. If necessary, the efficiency coil may have to be readjusted by half a turn, but the current at the output amplifier cathode should not exceed 200 ma. If foldover occurs after the high voltage adjustment, the horizontal efficiency coil should be readjusted. Focus, height, and vertical linearity controls may also require readjustment.

After the horizontal deflection system is correctly adjusted, all meters should be disconnected and the two cathode jumpers returned to their ground connection.

CHROMA BANDPASS ADJUSTMENT

Chroma bandpass adjustment can be performed in several different ways, depending on the test equipment available. In our example, the manufacturer recommends the use of an r-f modulator to modulate the color subcarrier r-f frequency with the video sweep signal. There is some test equipment available that contains the color subcarrier modulation, eliminating the need for a separate modulator. If neither equipment is available, a less accurate, but often quite satisfactory method can be used, as described later in this section. The color killer bias is replaced by −6 volts and the blanker tube is disabled by connecting −15 volts to its grid. I-F and tuner agc are the same as for i-f alignment. In general, the chroma alignment consists of three steps.

Step 1. Connect the sweep generator to the input of the bandpass amplifier. Sweep frequency setting should be between 0 and 5 mc and, if internal markers for this range are not available, video absorption markers from an external box can be used. Markers are required for the 3.58-mc, 4.08-mc, and 3.08-mc points. The video detector probe, or a circuit like that shown in Figure 22-6B, connects from the demodulator grid point to the oscilloscope. Tune the bandpass output transformer for a symmetrical curve with the 3.58-mc marker in the center.

Step 2. To align the input network to the bandpass amplifier, the signal is usually injected at the tuner mixer grid, just like the i-f signal. Either a combination sweep generator at video frequency, video markers, r-f modulators, and a signal generator must be used as shown in Figure 22-11, or else a generator containing all these elements can be connected to the tuner. The video detector scope probe is first advanced to the plate side of the bandpass amplifier, with that transformer bypassed with a series circuit of a 330-ohm resistor and 4-μfd capacitor. Now the scope will show the response of the video section and the bandpass amplifier input circuit. The chroma take-off coil is tuned for maximum peak at 3.58 mc. Adjust the two generators to keep the vtvm reading below 1.5 v dc.

(If the full test equipment described above is not available, another method is to connect a signal generator tuned to 3.58 mc to the first video amplifier grid and connect the vtvm through the video detector probe to the output of the bandpass amplifier. Then the chroma take-off coil is tuned for maximum vtvm reading.)

Step 3. With the connections of step 2 in place, remove the 330-ohm resistor and 4-μfd capacitor and return the video detector probe to the demodulator grid point. Now, the overall bandpass

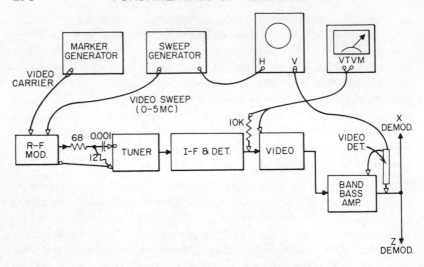

Fig. 22-11. Chroma bandpass alignment connections.

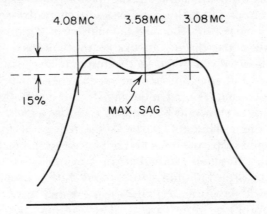

Fig. 22-12. Chroma bandpass reponse curve.

response can be observed and compared to that shown in Figure 22-12. The output transformer is readjusted for the correct peaks and the chroma take-off coil for minimum sag at the center. If the full test equipment complement is not available, this overall check cannot be made.

After the chroma bandpass alignment is completed, be sure to remove all leads and bias sources.

COLOR SYNC AND COLOR KILLER ALIGNMENT

To perform color sync and color killer alignment properly, a color bar generator, an oscilloscope, and a vtvm are required. Because the signals in this section are all around 3.58 mc, clip leads and probe connections should be kept short. The actual phase adjustments will vary with different color set models, but the alignment described below for the RCA CTC11 is typical for many other models as well.

The color bar generator is connected to the antenna terminals and all receiver controls are adjusted for normal color pictures. The tint or hue control is set to midrange and the color killer threshold control is turned counterclockwise to minimum.

Step 1. Short the grid of the burst gate amplifier to ground with a short clip lead. Connect the vtvm through the high impedance probe, or a 470K resistor, to one side of the color sync phase detector and tune the transformer coupling the local 3.58 mc from the oscillator to the phase detector for maximum vtvm reading. If the 3.58-mc oscillator is not operating, adjust the reactance-tube plate coil until the vtvm indicates the presence of 3.58 mc. Remove the clip lead grounding the burst gate amplifier grid.

Step 2. With the vtvm in place, peak the burst gate plate transformer to couple maximum signal to the phase detector. Make sure the 3.58-mc oscillator is locked-in by checking that the hues on the screen remain fixed.

Step 3. Ground the grid of the reactance tube. In the RCA CTC11 this is brought out as a test point that can be jumped to the chassis with a short clip lead. Now remove the vtvm probe and observe the color bars on the screen. Adjust the reactance control coil, in the plate of the reactance tube, until the colors in the bar pattern stand still or drift very slowly. Now remove the ground clip to the reactance tube grid and, if necessary, touch up the reactance control coil until the color bars correspond in hue to the prescribed pattern for that color bar generator. Reduce the generator output until a weak color picture is obtained. It may be necessary to touch up the reactance control coil again.

Step 4. To check the range of the tint control and optimize the adjustment of the phase detector transformer, the oscilloscope

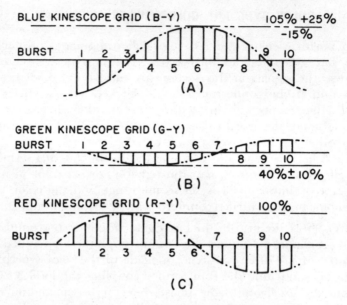

Fig. 22.13. Color bar waveforms at the picture tube control grids.

is connected to the $R-Y$ grid of the color picture tube. A waveform like that shown in Figure 22-13C should appear. Note that the sixth bar goes through zero. Adjustment of the tint or hue control should vary to phase sufficiently so that the fifth and seventh bars can be moved to the zero point. Touch-up of the phase detector transformer may be necessary to achieve this.

Step 5. The demodulator and matrix contain no adjustments, but their operation can be checked with the same test set-up as in step 4 above. Connect the oscilloscope to the $R-Y$, $B-Y$, and $G-Y$ control grids of the color picture tube and compare the waveforms with the waveforms shown in Figure 22-13.

Step 6. Adjust the color killer threshold first on a strong monochrome signal until the color just disappears from the screen. Next check on a relatively weak color signal to make sure that the killer bias does not block the color information.

CONCLUSION

The individual alignment procedures shown in this chapter cover all receiver sections that require the adjustment of tuned circuits. These alignment procedures require the proper test equipment and are generally performed on the bench. Another set of adjustments is available on all TV receivers for use by the set owner and the technician, but these are generally set in the home, without the need for any test equipment. In this category fall the brightness, contrast, focus, size, and linearity adjustments, and all of the color picture tube set-up adjustments described in detail at the end of Chapter 15.

APPENDIX 1
Bibliography

Anner, George E. *Elements of Television Systems.* Englewood Cliffs, N. J.: Prentice-Hall, Inc., 1961.

Buchsbaum, Walter H. *Color TV Servicing.* Englewood Cliffs, N. J.: Prentice-Hall, Inc., 1955.

Buchsbaum, Walter H. *Television Servicing.* Englewood Cliffs, N. J.: Prentice-Hall, Inc., Third Edition, 1958.

Cantor, Leon, and Harry Horstmann. *Repairing TV Remote Controls.* New York: John F. Rider Publisher, Inc., 1962.

Crowhurst, Norman H. *Basic Audio.* New York: John F. Rider Publisher, Inc., 1959.

Glasford, Glen M. *Fundamentals of Television Engineering.* New York: McGraw Hill, Inc., 1955.

Grob, Bernard. *Basic Television.* New York: McGraw Hill, Inc., Third Edition, 1964.

Hazeltine Corp. Laboratory Staff. *Color Television Receiver Practices.* New York: John F. Rider Publisher, Inc., 1955.

Lytel, Alan. *How to Service UHF TV.* New York: John F. Rider Publisher, Inc., 1964.

Mayers, M. A., and R. D. Chipp. *Closed Circuit TV System Planning.* New York: John F. Rider Publisher, Inc., 1957.

Middleton, Robert G. *TV Troubleshooting and Repair.* New York: John F. Rider Publisher, Inc., Second Edition, 1963.

Rider Laboratory Staff. *TV Picture Tube—Chassis Guide.* New York: John F. Rider Publisher, Inc., 1957.

Schure, Alexander. *Basic Transistors.* New York: John F. Rider Publisher, Inc., 1961.

Towers, T. D. *Transistor Television Receivers.* New York: John F. Rider Publisher, Inc., 1963.

"Proceedings of the IRE." Second Color Television Issue, Vol. 42, No. 1, January 1954.

"Proceedings of the IRE." Standards: Color TV Terms, Vol. 43, No. 6, June 1955.

APPENDIX 2
The RCA CTC 16

INDEX